McKeough

McKeough

fishes of the great barrier reef

by warren e. burgess & dr. herbert r. axelrod

1. *Chaetodon pelewensis* Kner. One of the butterflyfishes of the southern Pacific. Photo by Roger Steene.

pacific
marine
fishes

book 7

ISBN 0-87666-129-0

Distributed in the U.S.A. by T.F.H. Publications, Inc., 211 West Sylvania Avenue, P.O. Box 27, Neptune City, N.J. 07753; in England by T.F.H. (Gt. Britain) Ltd., 13 Nutley Lane, Reigate, Surrey; in Canada to the book store and library trade by Clarke, Irwin & Company, Clarwin House, 791 St. Clair Avenue West, Toronto 10, Ontario; in Canada to the pet trade by Rolf C. Hagen Ltd., 3225 Sartelon Street, Montreal 382, Quebec; in Southeast Asia by Y.W. Ong, 9 Lorong 36 Geylang, Singapore 14; in Australia and the south Pacific by Pet Imports Pty. Ltd., P.O. Box 149, Brookvale 2100, N.S.W., Australia. Published by T.F.H. Publications Inc. Ltd., The British Crown Colony of Hong Kong.

TABLE OF CONTENTS

1. Family HETERODONTIDAE (*Port Jackson Sharks*) .. 1664
2. Family ORECTOLOBIDAE
   (*Wobbegongs and Catsharks*) 1666
3. Family MYLIOBATIDAE
   (*Eagle Rays and their relatives*) 1672
4. Family DASYATIDAE (*Stingrays*) 1673
5. Family RHINOBATIDAE
   (*Guitarfishes and Shovel-nosed Rays*) 1677
6. Family APOGONIDAE (*Cardinalfishes*) 1681
7. Family LABRIDAE (*Wrasses*) 1729
8. Family SIGANIDAE (*Rabbitfishes*) 1753
9. Family AULOSTOMIDAE (*Trumpetfishes*) 1799
10. Family ECHENEIDAE (*Remoras and Suckerfishes*) ... 1803
11. Family BATRACHOIDIDAE
    (*Toadfishes and Midshipmen*) 1821
12. Family SERRANIDAE (*Groupers*) 1839
13. Family LETHRINIDAE (*Emperor Bream*) 1880
14. Family THERAPONIDAE (*Tigerfishes*) 1887
15. Family CEPOLIDAE (*Bandfishes*) 1888
16. Family MONOCENTRIDAE (*Pinecone Fishes*) 1889
17. Family OSTRACIONTIDAE (*Trunkfishes*) 1899
18. Family TETRAODONTIDAE (*Puffers*) 1903
19. Family MONACANTHIDAE (*Filefishes*) 1905

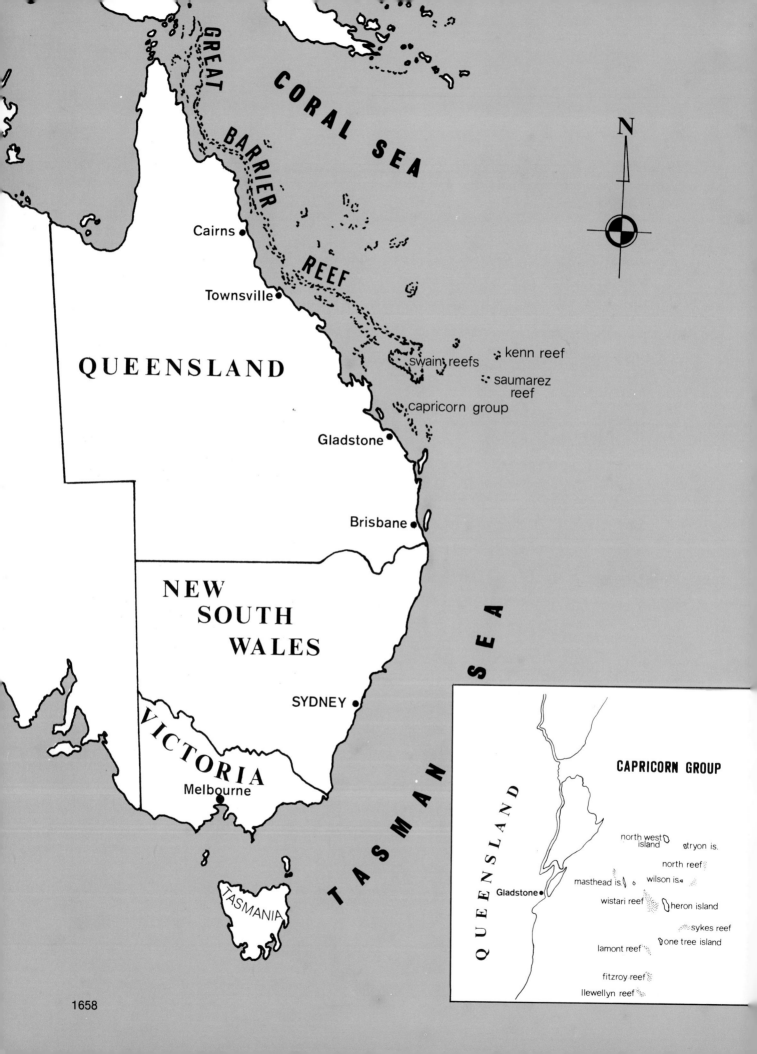

GREAT BARRIER REEF

CORAL SEA

Cairns

Townsville

QUEENSLAND

swain reefs
kenn reef
saumarez reef
capricorn group

Gladstone

Brisbane

NEW SOUTH WALES

T A S M A N   S E A

SYDNEY

VICTORIA

Melbourne

TASMANIA

N

CAPRICORN GROUP

QUEENSLAND

Gladstone

north west island
tryon is.

north reef

masthead is.
wilson is.

wistari reef
heron island

sykes reef

lamont reef
one tree island

fitzroy reef

llewellyn reef

1658

FISHES OF THE GREAT BARRIER REEF

INTRODUCTION

Off the northeastern coast of Australia, from about 24°S latitude north almost to the coast of New Guinea, lies the greatest development of coral reefs in the world, the Great Barrier Reef of Australia. Its 1,260 miles are not unbroken reef as the name might suggest, but a combination of numerous coral reefs, outcrops and islands occupying an area of approximately 80,000 square miles. Although the barrier reef is not solid, entrance to the inner waters can be made only at certain passages where there are navigable channels. It provides a natural barrier for almost the entire coast of Queensland from the waters of the South Pacific Ocean and is separated from the mainland by a channel where depths to 30 fathoms are commonly encountered. The reef itself lies anywhere from 7 to 42 miles from Queensland and can usually be reached by boat (a number of tour boats are available for several of the more beautiful cays or islands). As one gets further from the mainland the coral growth gets more luxurient, unhampered by the detrimental effects of fresh water and silt that are discharged from the many river mouths in Queensland.

The Great Barrier Reef stretches from near temperate waters to the tropical waters in the vicinity of New Guinea and probably houses one of the richest and most diverse faunas of the world. The great variety of corals grow in such profusion that they form at times veritable underwater forests which provide protection for small fishes and invertebrates which attract, and become food for, the larger fishes. At low tide in many areas the corals poke their heads above water but in a short time are again covered. If they are exposed for too long a time they will die; if they are exposed to fresh water or silt for too long a period they will also die. Aside from these physical dangers, there are biological ones as well, such as the recent discovery of the attacks on coral reefs by coral eating starfishes of the genus *Acanthaster*. And of course man has stepped in at times to crunch these beautiful and delicate creatures under his heavy feet or to cart them away by the carloads for land fill. Yet these small animals have survived to build these immense structures called coral reefs. A coral animal is generally small, visible to the naked eye, but perhaps better seen under low magnification. They look like anemones but secrete a calcareous skeleton —this skeleton is the part remaining after a coral branch or head is thoroughly cleaned. Each "hole" in the skeleton housed a

2. Sometimes the tide becomes low enough to expose the tops of the corals. Reef crest, Wistari Reef. Photo by Walter Deas.

3. An aerial view of some of the reefline of Heron Island. Photo by Keith Gillett, taken at 1,100 feet.

coral animal (called a polyp). Most of the fishes in this book are dependent upon the coral for some aspect of their life, whether it be protection, food, or just a place to rest.

One estimate of the number of species of fishes found on or near the Great Barrier Reef is 1,500 (including the fresh water fishes of Queensland, which are not included in this book). Some of the fishes depicted here are recognizable from earlier books for they are part of the vast Indo-Pacific fauna covered in this series. Others are definitely distinct, these being the endemic part of the Great Barrier Reef fish fauna. The fauna most closely related to that of the Great Barrier Reef is probably that of Melanesia, which was covered in *Pacific Marine Fishes* Book 6. Book 8 will deal with southern Australian fishes, more temperate in nature, plus those of New Zealand, which are definitely temperate, and a small island, Lord Howe, on the borderline between the temperate and tropical faunas.

Aside from the endemic and Indo-Pacific portions of the fauna, the Great Barrier Reef fishes show certain affinities northward, either with the East Indies or, further north, with Japan, the ranges of some fishes extending from Japan to the Great Barrier Reef.

Anyone who has ever gone diving on the Great Barrier Reef, and both of us have, must marvel at the panorama that is before his eyes. The photos on these pages can just begin to reveal the wonders that can be found there, to whet one's appetite for more spectacular views. There are areas in this world that do rival the Great Barrier Reef for beauty, the crystal clear waters of the Bahamas for example, but nowhere can you find over 1,000 miles of such underwater fantasylands.

For scientists there is a great deal to be done on the Great Barrier Reef. The fish fauna is just beginning to become known and there are still a great number of species yet to be discovered and named. Scientific (or other) expeditions are carefully controlled so that there is no decimation of the fauna. The Australian government realizes that they have one of the great wonders of the world under their protection and have taken steps to protect it. It is partially for this reason that there are not many exporters of marine fishes in that area. But there are some, and occasionally a U.S. importer will get his hands on some of the unusual Australian fishes such as *Chaetodon rainfordi* or *Monocentris gloriamaris*. The Australians have some interesting common names for their fishes,

4.
One Tree Island,
where scientists may
obtain permission to
make collections
from time to time.
Photo by Dr. Gerald
R. Allen.

5.
Some of the damsel-
fishes (*Abudefduf
whitleyi*) of Dixie
Reef, Great Barrier
Reef. Photo by Dr.
Gerald R. Allen (10-15
feet deep).

6. In some areas there are fishes and corals as far as the eye can see. Photo by Dr. Gerald R. Allen, Spur Reef (about 25 feet deep):

names which will probably not be familiar to most Americans but which will be included in this book from time to time. *Pterois antennata*, for example, will become the butterfly-cod, *Chromis caeruleus* is known there as the blue puller, and *Dascyllus aruanus* as the banded humbug.

The names on these fishes were more difficult to arrive at than for previous books in this series since most of the photos were taken *in situ* and specimens were not available for examination. Dr. Gerald R.

Allen, who provided many of the excellent photos in this book, also provided his own identifications for us. He has worked in Australia for the past few years (he is now Curator of Fishes for the Western Australian Museum) and is familiar with the fish fauna of the Great Barrier Reef, having made many collections there for the Australian Museum.

The photos for this book were taken for the most part by some of the finest underwater photographers in the world:

Walter Deas, Allan Power, Keith Gillett, etc. Dr. Gerald (Jerry) Allen, fast becoming an expert in underwater photography, and Roger Steene, another up and coming photographer of sea life, helped round out the photo content of this volume.

It is hoped that once again the bringing to light of many of the Australian fishes through photographs will help aquarists and scientists in their particular endeavors. The aquarist can perhaps put names on some of the fishes he has seen or purchased from Australia or elsewhere; scientists can perhaps see for the first time the animals, which they have been working with as preserved museum specimens, in their natural environment and in full color.

7. In other areas the corals are plentiful but the fishes are not as abundant. Photo by Dr. Gerald R. Allen, Spur Reef (about 30 feet deep).

Family HETERODONTIDAE
PORT JACKSON SHARKS

The southern part of the Great Barrier Reef is a mixing zone where the reef fauna comes in contact and overlaps in many cases with the more temperate water fishes that live in the south. That is apparently why such species as the Port Jackson sharks have been recorded from Queensland. It is also possible that some of the southern forms move north along the Great Barrier Reef, not in the warm shallow waters but fairly deep where water temperatures are not so high. Both of the Australian Port Jackson sharks have been recorded from Queensland, though the larger part of their range lies to the south.

There is a question as to whether there are two genera involved, *Heterodontus* and *Gyropleurodus*. The differences between the genera are not great, being concerned with the shape of the supraorbital ridges and the shape of the teeth. The species

shown here would be considered to belong to the genus *Gyropleurodus* if the distinction were made, as opposed to *Heterodontus portusjacksoni*, the other Australian representative of this group.

Heterodontus, or *Gyropleurodus* if you wish, *galeatus* is a small (about 4 feet at full size) harmless shark that inhabits waters to a depth of 100 meters. It feeds on molluscs, crabs, and sea urchins, this last mentioned commonly being the purple sea urchin, *Centrostephanus rodgersii*, which stains the lips and teeth of the shark a reddish-purple color.

In the middle winter months this shark is encountered more often inshore where it apparently moves in to breed. Spawning takes place late in the winter or early spring, and the eggs take at least five months (even up to nine months) to hatch.

8. *Heterodontus galeatus* (Gunther). This diver is showing us the spines preceding the two dorsal fins of this crested Port Jackson shark. ·Photo by Walter Deas.

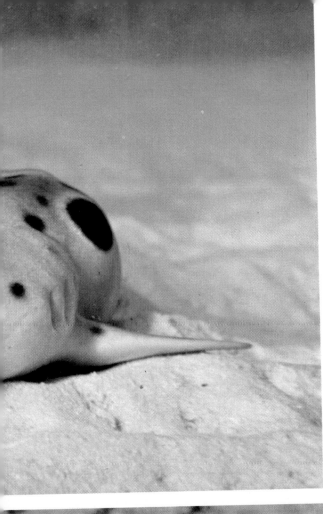

The young shark is perfectly formed and only 6 inches long. It was some of the egg cases, turning up in Queensland waters, which first indicated that these sharks were there. The males are generally much smaller and slimmer than the females. After spawning the adults disappear until the following year.

The small size and often colorful patterns of these sharks make them candidates for large home aquaria. A 100-gallon tank should be the smallest one considered if any sizable shark is obtained. Crabs or shrimp would make good food in captivity.

9. *Hemiscyllium ocellatum* (Bonnaterre). A pretty and harmless shark that attains a length of only 3 feet. Photo by Allan Power.

10. *Hemiscyllium ocellatum* (Bonnaterre). The epaulette shark is commonly found in shallow water among the corals. Photo by Allan Power.

Family ORECTOLOBIDAE
WOBBEGONGS AND CATSHARKS

One of the common sharks seen among the coral growths of the Great Barrier Reef is the epaulette shark, *Hemiscyllium ocellatum*. It is small, normally growing only to about three feet in length, and harmless. The color pattern is quite distinctive, with the large dark ocellated spot above the pectorals and the numerous dark spots covering the upper portion of the body and the fins. Only one other shark in Australian waters has the large ocellated spot on its side (*H. trispeculare*) but that one is covered with small brownish dots instead of large ones and is referred to as the freckled shark. The epaulette shark should make an interesting aquarium inhabitant and is very likely easy to keep.

The wobbegongs or carpet sharks can be differentiated by a combination of color pattern and number and type of cirri. *Orectolobus ogilbyi*, for example, has a nearly continuous row of branched cirri on the head, whereas the other wobbegongs have only scattered cirri. The pattern is variable and usually quite attractive. Young ones would probably make good aquarium fishes, but they grow very large (to 12 feet in length) and because of their strong jaws and sharp pointed teeth have to be considered potentially dangerous. One report says that if this shark were to grab somebody, it would be difficult to release the shark's jaws. The tasseled wobbegong, as it is called in Australia, is encountered in shallow water, anywhere from about 6 to 60 feet, in the protection of caves or ledges during the day. But at night it is up and about searching for food. It dines on fish, crustaceans, and octopuses which are also nocturnal.

The banded wobbegong, *O. ornatus*, also has a pleasing color pattern of dark bands and light spots. It does not grow as large as *O. ogilbyi* (to only 7 feet), but should still be regarded as potentially dangerous. It is also common on the Great Barrier Reef among the rocks and coral, especially where there are good growths of algae where it can blend into the background more easily.

11. *Orectolobus ornatus* (De Vis). The banded wobbegong is a well-marked shark but aquarists beware—it grows to 7 feet. Photo by Walter Deas.

12. *Orectolobus ornatus* (De Vis). This shark ranges from southeastern New Guinea along the east and south coasts of Australia. Photo by Allan Power.

13.
Orectolobus ornatus
(De Vis). Adult. It is easy
to see why this shark
belongs to the carpet
sharks, with its
flattened, ornate
appearance. Photo by
Allan Power.

14. *Orectolobus ogilbyi* Regan. The tassled wobbegong gets its name from the fringed tentacles (branched dermal lobes) that edge the mouth. Photo by Allan Power.

15. *Galeocerdo cuvieri* (Peron and Lesueur). Tiger shark. The tail end of the eagle ray (opposite page) can be seen sticking out of this shark's mouth. Photo by Allan Power.

16.
Triaenodon obesus
(Ruppell). White-tipped
reef shark. This is a
widespread common
shark found throughout
the Indo-Pacific. Photo
of a 5-foot individual by
Dr. Gerald R. Allen (20
feet deep).

17. *Aetobatus narinari* (Euphrasen). Spotted eagle ray. The tiger shark took two big chunks from this ray.
Note the size of the bites as compared to the diver. Photo by Allan Power.

Family MYLIOBATIDAE
EAGLE RAYS AND THEIR RELATIVES

There are three genera of eagle rays reported from Queensland waters, namely *Aetobatus*, *Myliobatus*, and *Rhinoptera*, separable by shape of the snout and the number of rows of teeth in each jaw. Otherwise these rays are quite similar in appearance and easily recognizable as eagle rays. *Rhinoptera* is distinctive in having two separate lobes to the snout; *R. javanica*, which occurs in Australia, has been given the common name cow-nosed ray. *Aetobatus* and *Myliobatus* are more difficult to distinguish, *Aetobatus* having a single row of teeth in each jaw and *Myliobatus* having more than three rows. A species of *Myliobatus* was illustrated in PMF-4 (p. 1076) and *Aetobatus* is shown below.

Aetobatus narinari has a large range, including most of the warmer Pacific, Indian and Atlantic Oceans, and has accumulated a number of common names in different areas. It is known as the jumping ray, duckbill ray, and even bonnet skate, but the most popular name throughout its range is the spotted eagle ray. It receives the name jumping ray from its habit of leaping out of the water at intervals. Females are said to give birth during these leaps, each new-born ray being released at the peak of a leap.

The spotted eagle ray gets quite large, with a wingspan of over 10 feet and a weight exceeding 200 pounds, although most of those encountered are much smaller with disc widths of four to five feet. One of the larger rays was attacked by a shark and two large pieces were bitten off before the shark was dispatched by a power-head spear. The result can be seen on page 1671. The tail spine was included in one of these pieces but apparently had little or no effect on the shark. One of the pieces was reported to weigh 15 pounds. The attacking shark was identified as a tiger shark, *Galeocerdo cuvieri*, one of the more dangerous and feared species.

18. *Aetobatus narinari* (Euphrasen). Alternate names for this ray are duckbill ray, jumping ray, and beaked eagle ray. Photo by Allan Power.

Family DASYATIDAE
STINGRAYS

There are a number of stingrays to be found in Queensland waters. They have been divided into several genera depending upon the shape of the disc, length and thickness of the tail, presence or absence and shape of fins, number of tail spines, and color.

Urolophus, which is pictured below, is uniformly colored, has a relatively short, stout tail, a near circular disc, a caudal fin, and a tail spine. *Taeniura* is similar but lacks the caudal fin. It also is easily distinguishable because the only species on the Great Barrier Reef is *T. lymma*, which has bright blue spots on its back. A third genus, *Gymnura*, has a more angular disc which is very wide, as well as a slender tail and vestigial dorsal fin. *Urogymnus* is distinguishable in part by its lack of a serrated spine on the tail. The three genera which have long whip-like tails can be distinguished partly by the tail folds, *Himantura* lacking them, *Pastinachus* having a broad fold, and *Dasyatis* having narrow tail folds, although *Pastinachus* is probably only a subgenus of *Dasyatis*.

The common stingray, or stingaree if you prefer, has a broad depth range in Queensland, occurring in water over 300 feet deep as well as in shallow water over a sand bottom as shown in the accompanying photo. *Urogymnus africanus* is less common in Australian waters though it does have a considerable geographic range. It attains a width of about two feet, or about twice that of the common stingray.

The cowtail or fantail ray, *Dasyatis* (or *Pastinachus*) *sephen*, grows much larger, disc widths of six feet being reported. This species is fairly common in Australian waters in shallow areas, especially on the incoming tides. It has a long tail with a broad black feather-like cutaneous fold below it, which is characteristic of the species, as well as a barbed spine which can be used with great efficiency. Normally it is safe to hold a stingray at arms length by the spiracle, but not with this ray. It is able to bend the tail far enough to send the spine into the hand holding it that way. The barbs inflict a jagged or puncture type wound which should be cared for as soon as possible. The poison is rendered less effective if heat is applied. Allan Power recommends a hot water bottle.

19. *Urolophus testaceus* (Muller and Henle). Common stingaree. This ray is commonly found in shallow water on sand flats. Photo by Allan Power.

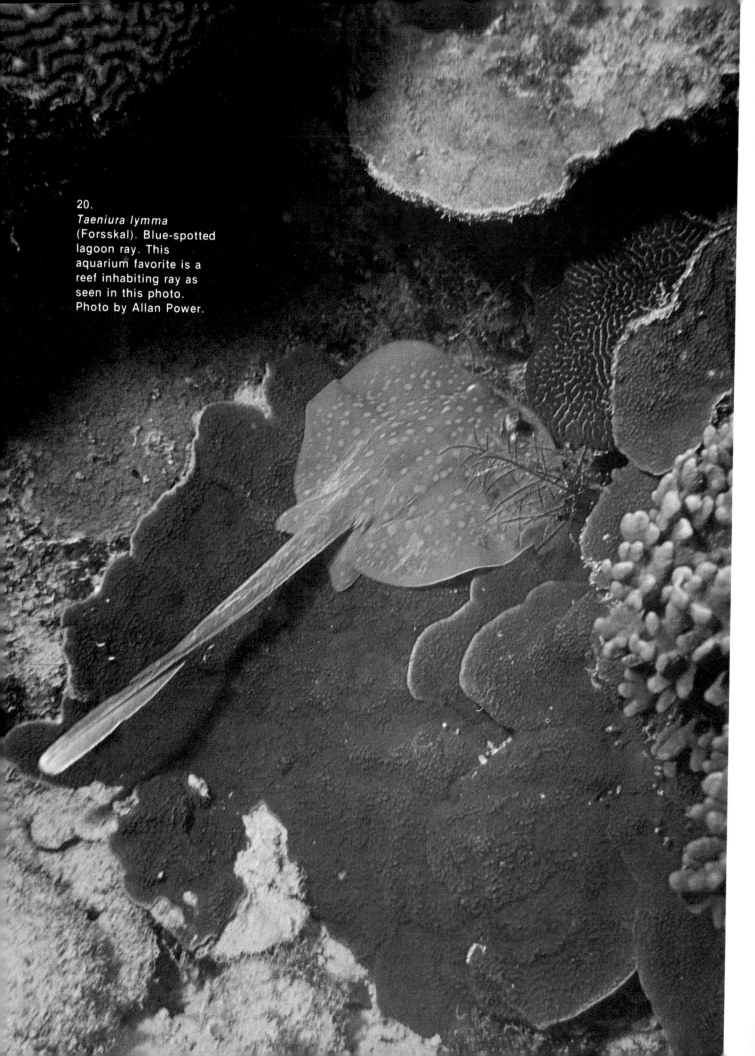

20.
Taeniura lymma
(Forsskal). Blue-spotted
lagoon ray. This
aquarium favorite is a
reef inhabiting ray as
seen in this photo.
Photo by Allan Power.

21. *Urogymnus africanus* (Schneider). Thorny ray. The "thorns" are sharp tubercles (tubercular scales) on its back and tail. Photo by Allan Power.

22. ?*Dasyatis* (*Pastinachus*) *sephen* (Forsskal). Cowtail or fantail ray. This ray attains a disc width of some 6 feet. Photo by Walter Deas, Wistari Reef (30 feet).

23. *?Dasyatis (Pastinachus) sephen* (Forsskal). It is possible that this is not *D. sephen* but *D. brevicaudata*) without specimens it is difficult to tell. Note the purple-blue *Assessor* swimming close by. Photo by Allan Power.

Family RHINOBATIDAE
GUITARFISHES AND
SHOVEL-NOSED RAYS

There are several shovel-nosed rays found throughout Australia. On the Barrier Reef around Queensland five genera are recognized: *Rhina, Rhynchobatus, Rhinobatos, Aptychotrema,* and *Trygonorrhina*. They are differentiated by position of the anterior dorsal fin (above the ventrals in the first two genera, well behind ventrals in the other three) and the shape of the snout (broad and semicircular in *Rhina*, long, narrow, and pointed in *Rhynchobatus*, long, shovel-shaped, and pointed in *Rhinobatos* and *Aptychotrema,* and more obtuse in *Trygonorrhina*). *Rhinobatos* and *Aptychotrema*, which may not be distinct genera, are separated by the angle of the nostrils (oblique in *Rhinobatos*, nearly transverse in *Aptychotrema*). *Rhina ancylostomus*, which occurs in Australian waters, appeared in PMF-4 (p. 1072-1073); *Rhinobatos armatus* is shown below.

The common shovel-nosed ray, *Rhinobatos armatus*, may be found through-out the Queensland coast but is apparently more common in the northern sectors. Individuals of seven feet have been reported, although more probably sizes of three to four feet will be encountered. Although mostly found in sandy marine areas, these fishes are able to enter brackish or fresh water areas. They are said to spawn in fresh water and the young can often be seen in the shallow inshore waters. Typically the color pattern is sandy or brownish colored, matching the bottom on which they live. They will settle on the sand and bury themselves partially under the sand, making them difficult to spot. If they are approached too closely they will take off in a burst of speed with sand being scattered in all directions. They will move away from the disturbance a short distance and settle into the sand once again.

The food consists of sand dwelling animals such as crustaceans and molluscs which they are able to dispatch with their pavement-like teeth.

24. *Rhinobatos armatus* (Gray). Common shovel-nose ray. This harmless ray looks almost shark-like with an elongate body. Photo by Roger Steene.

25. *Apogon* (*Gronovichthys*) *aureus* (Lacepede). Ring-tailed cardinalfish. The band surrounding the caudal peduncle and the blue lines around the head make this cardinalfish readily identifiable. Photo by Dr. Herbert R. Axelrod.

26. *Apogon* sp. Similar to *A. diversus* of the Philippine Islands and may be a new species. Photo by Walter Deas, Wistari Reef (50 feet deep).

27. A large school of *Apogon* sp. hovering near the protection of the coral *Acropora*. Note the young *Bodianus axillaris* nearby. Photo by Allan Power.

28. *Apogon* sp. The brassy golden color of these cardinalfishes makes them candidates for the aquarium trade. Photo by Allan Power.

Family APOGONIDAE
CARDINALFISHES

Cardinalfishes are relatively common in Australian waters, especially the warmer areas such as the Queensland coast. They are divided there into six genera, some of which are not universally accepted by ichthyologists. *Apogon* of course is the largest genus of cardinalfishes on the Great Barrier Reef, with at least two dozen species. *Cheilodipterus*, distinguished by the distinct canines, is represented by only a few species.

Siphamia, a genus identified by the silvery tube-like prolongation along the ventral surface of the body, occurs on the Great Barrier Reef with two or more species included, but is separate from *Adenapogon*. *Adenapogon*, if accepted, may be distinguished from *Siphamia* by the six dorsal fin spines, the 7, 8, or 10 dorsal soft rays, and the shape of the body, which is slender and elongate. The species involved are *S. roseigaster*, *S. cuneiceps*, and *S. woodi*, all Australian species. *Siphamia roseigaster* is a small 3-inch fish that occurs in estuaries and harbors along the Queensland coast. It is nocturnal and often captured by night by fishermen trawling for prawns. The characteristic silvery tubes are thought to be luminous organs. *Fodifoa*, which also has a silvery tube, is sometimes included in *Siphamia*. If separated, it is done so on the basis that *Fodifoa* has an incomplete lateral line.

The sixth genus, *Foa*, is also separated from *Apogon* by the presence of an incomplete lateral line, but is just as often included within that genus.

The cardinalfishes seem to have invaded many habitats in Queensland, from brackish to fresh water estuaries and rivers to the coral reef. They often occur in large schools on the reef, taking refuge in the branching corals that are abundant there. Smaller individuals may make use of the long-spined sea urchins, sharing this shelter with various other fishes.

29. *Apogon* sp. Hiding in the corals did not prevent these cardinalfishes from being photographed. Photo by Allan Power.

30.
Apogon doderleini
Jordan and Snyder.
There are many striped
cardinalfishes but few
with such broad head
stripes and narrow body
stripes. Photo of a
3-inch individual at
Lizard Island by Dr.
Gerald R. Allen
(10 feet deep).

31. *Cheilodipterus quinquelineatus* Cuvier and Valenciennes. Five-striped percale. A solitary individual venturing out from the protection of the ledge. Photo by Walter Deas. Heron Island at 35 feet.

32.
Apogon hartzfeldi
Bleeker. Hartzfeld's
cardinalfish. A pretty
little cardinalfish that
grows to a length of
about 4-5 inches. Photo
by Roger Steene.

33. *Apogon aroubiensis* Hombron and Jacquinot. This species may be referred to as *Lovamia aroubiensis* by the Australians. Photo by Allan Power.

34. A school of young cardinalfishes in the darkness of a cave. Notice how tightly packed they are. Photo by Allan Power.

35.
Apogon thermalis
Bleeker. Bar-cheeked
cardinalfish. This 3-inch
cardinalfish was photo-
graphed by Dr. Gerald R.
Allen at Lizard Island in
16 feet of water.

36.
Apogon leptacanthus
Bleeker. Threadfin
cardinalfish. This group
of 3-inch cardinalfishes
was found in 6 feet of
water by Dr. Gerald R.
Allen. Lizard Island.

37.
Apogon fragilis Smith. A
very delicately colored
cardinalfish with the
caudal fin tips, a spot at
the base of the caudal
fin, and the eyes black.
Photo by Dr. Gerald R.
Allen at Lizard Island
(35 feet deep).

38. *Gymnothorax flavimarginata* (Ruppell). Leopard moray eel. This is how you usually see a moray eel, with its head poking out of its hole to investigate the diver. Photo by Allan Power at Wistari Reef (95 feet deep).

39. *Gymnothorax favagineus* Bloch and Schneider. Tessellated reef eel. The common name was derived from one of the synonyms, *G. tessellata*. Photo by Allan Power.

40. *Gymnothorax* sp. being cleaned by *Labroides dimidiatus*, which seems to be safe from the moray while it performs its duties. Photo by Walter Deas at Heron Island.

41. *Flammeo sammara* (Forsskal). Blood-spot squirrelfish. The common name refers to the dark red spot in the dorsal fin. Photo by Walter Deas.

42. *Flammeo sammara* (Forsskal). This species may go under several other names, one of which is *Kutaflammeo sammara*. Photo by Walter Deas on Kenn Reef (20 feet deep).

43. *Flammeo sammara* (Forsskal). This photo shows the differentiation of the distinctive dorsal fin spot from the red of the remaining portion of the fin. Photo by **Allan Power**.

44. *Adioryx cornutus* (Bleeker). Red-and-white squirrelfish. This species has also been called the horned squirrelfish. Photo by **Allan Power**.

45.
Adioryx rubra (Forsskal). Red
soldierfish. A wide ranging
species that attains a length of
almost one foot. Photo by Walter
Deas.

46. *Adioryx rubra* (Forsskal). During the day this species can most easily be found by looking into caves or
other dark places. Photo by Walter Deas at Heron Island (20 feet deep).

47. *Adioryx spinifer* (Forsskal). Scarlet-fin soldierfish. The camera flash catches this squirrelfish in its hiding place. Photo by Allan Power.

48. *Adioryx spinifer* (Forsskal). The spination of the head can be seen in this close-up view of the scarlet-fin soldierfish. Photographed at 70 feet by Allan Power (Wistari Reef).

49. *Myripristis multiradiatus* Gunther. This species can be found at depths of some 25 feet or more. Photo by Allan Power.

50. *Myripristis murdjan* (Forsskal). Blotch-eye. The common name probably stems from the dark mark in the upper part of the eye. Photo by Allan Power.

51. A school of pempherids may pick up a stray cardinalfish or two. The pempherids have a single dorsal fin whereas cardinalfishes have two. Photo by Walter Deas at Wistari Reef (40 feet deep).

52.
Amphiprion melanopus Bleeker. Dusky anemonefish. This pair of anemonefish nestles among the tentacles of *Physobranchia*, the most abundant anemone on the Great Barrier Reef. Photo by Allan Power at Wistari Reef (30 feet deep).

53. *Amphiprion melanopus* in the anemone *Physobrachia*. This anemonefish is usually found in pairs on the Great Barrier Reef. Photo by Keith Gillett.

54. *Amphiprion melanopus* Bleeker. The anemone in the background has retracted, leaving the fish on its own. This gives us a good view of the entire fish. Photo by Roger Steene.

55. *Amphiprion melanopus* Bleeker. The pectoral fin when spread looks very paddle-like. The branching of the fin rays is clearly seen. Photo by Walter Deas at Wistari Reef (30 feet deep).

57. *Amphiprion akindynos* Allen. The yellow-faced anemonefish is fairly common in Queensland. Photo by Allan Power, Wistari Reef (30 feet deep).

56. *Amphiprion akindynos* Allen. This fish has been known in Australia as *A. unimaculatus*. Photo by Allan Power, One Tree Island (50 feet deep).

58. *Amphiprion akindynos* Allen. This species is very similar to *A. clarkii* but according to Dr. Allen that species is not found on the Great Barrier Reef. Photo by Allan Power.

59. *Amphiprion akindynos* Allen. Anemonefishes will come out of the anemone for bits of food that might float or swim by. Photo by Allan Power.

60. *Amphiprion akindynos* Allen. Notice that the head band on this fish is no longer connected on its nape. Photo by Allan Power.

61. *Amphiprion akindynos* Allen. Anemonefishes can be pretty brave when remaining in contact with their anemone, but get too close and they dive among the tentacles. Photo by Walter Deas, Wistari Reef (10 feet deep).

62. *Amphiprion perideraion* Bleeker. Sometimes anemones are grouped together forming a carpet of tentacles which house many anemonefishes. Photo by Walter Deas at Heron Island (15 feet deep).

63. *Amphiprion perideraion* Bleeker. Two anemonefishes pick at the mouth of the anemone, which is located in the center of the disc. Photo by Allan Power.

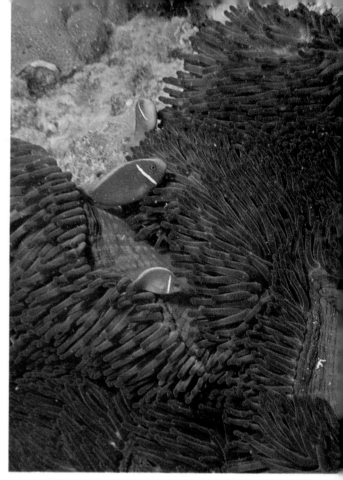

64. *Amphiprion perideraion* Bleeker. The lavender color-ed object is part of the anemone. They can be very beautiful, and aquarists have kept tanks with anemones and nothing else. Photo by Allan Power at Wistari Reef (30 feet deep).

65. *Amphiprion perideraion* Bleeker. This appears to be a colony of anemones although single ones can get quite large—several feet across in some cases. Photo by Allan Power.

66. *Amphiprion akindynos,* adult, Great Barrier Reef. Photo by W. Deas.

67. *Amphiprion perideraion* Bleeker and *Dascyllus trimaculatus* (Ruppell) share anemones although the *Dascyllus* is found more often in the protection of corals. Photo by Allan Power.

68.
Corals (here *Stylophora mordax*) provide protection for many small fishes. Note the various species in this photo. Photo by Walter Deas at Masthead Island, Queensland.

69. *Dascyllus reticulatus* (Richardson). Reticulated puller. When in good shape the white of the sides is very bright. When frightened, it gets very grayish or dark. Photo by Walter Deas.

70. *Dascyllus trimaculatus* (Ruppell). White-spot puller. These are young fish that have taken refuge in an anemone. Photo by Walter Deas.

71. Staghorn coral, *Acropora*, seems to be one of the favorite hiding places of damsels and other fishes. The coral is very sharp and many divers receive multiple cuts if they get tangled up in a growth of *Acropora*. Photo by Allan Power.

72.
Chromis nitidus
(Whitley). Shining
puller. A small group of
damselfishes gathers at
what appears to be a
cleaning station. Photo
by Dr. Gerald R. Allen of
3-inch individuals at One
Tree Island (30 feet
deep).

73. *Chromis nitidus* (Whitley). The color pattern is very distinctive and identification of this species is easy. Photo of a 2-inch individual at One Tree Island by Dr. Gerald R. Allen (40 feet deep).

74. *Chromis ternatensis* (Bleeker). Species after species can be seen close to some stands of coral (here *Acropora*). Even collectors find the going rough when chasing these fishes as their nets are torn to shreds. Photo by Allan Power.

75.
Chromis chrysurus
(Bliss). This species is
usually found feeding in
large aggregations over
beds of live coral to
which they retire when
approached. Photo by
Dr. Gerald R. Allen at
Opal Reef (40 feet deep).

76. A combination of damselfishes and butterflyfishes. The blue-green damsel is the blue puller (*Chromis caeru-leus*), the yellow damsel is *Pomacentrus amboinensis*, and the butterflyfishes are *Chaetodon trifasciatus* and *C. plebeius*. Photo by Allan Power.

77.
Chromis atripectoralis Welander and Schultz. Although resembling the blue puller, this species differs in having a black spot in the axil of the pectoral fin. Photo by Dr. Gerald R. Allen of a 3-inch individual from Heron Island (20 feet deep).

78.
Chromis weberi Fowler and Bean. The characteristic dark edges to the caudal fin are almost lost in the dark background. Photo by Dr. Gerald R. Allen of a 3-inch individual at Heron Island (20 feet deep).

79.
Chromis opercularis (Gunther). This species may be found around the reef in depths of 10-80 feet. Photo of a 4-inch fish by Dr. Gerald R. Allen at Heron Island (40 feet deep).

80.
Chromis atripectoralis Welander and Schultz and *Chromis caeruleus* (Cuvier). This may all be one species, but dark pectoral axils can be seen in some of the fishes. Photo by Walter Deas.

81. *Chromis caeruleus* (Cuvier). It is not common to see a single individual of the blue puller alone on the reef. Photo by Allan Power.

82. *Abudefduf flavipinnis* Allen and Robertson. This species also has a limited distribution, being found from the Solomon Islands and New Guinea to the Sydney area of Australia. Photo by Dr. Gerald R. Allen of an inch-and-a-half individual from One Tree Island (6 feet deep).

83. *Abudefduf flavipinnis* Allen and Robertson. This fish is usually encountered around dead coral rubble near sandy areas. Photo by Dr. Gerald R. Allen at One Tree Island (6 feet deep).

84.
Abudefduf (Glyphido-dontops) unimaculatus (Cuvier). This is one of the less colorful of the damselfishes; even the juveniles are brownish. Photo of a 3-inch individual at One Tree Island by Dr. Gerald R. Allen.

85.
Abudefduf (Glyphido-dontops) biocellatus (Quoy and Gaimard). Blue-banded damsel-fish. The three species on this page are very similar, with the one above even exhibiting a light streak through the body at times. Photo of a 3-inch fish by Dr. Gerald R. Allen at One Tree Island (4 feet deep).

86.
Abudefduf (Glyphido-dontops) leucopomus (Lesson). This fish is in what is called the "*amabilis*" phase according to Dr. Gerald R. Allen. *Abudefduf amabilis* is now a synonym of *leuco-pomus*. Photo by Dr. Gerald R. Allen at One Tree Island (2 feet deep).

87.
Abudefduf whitleyi Allen
and Robertson. One can
see feeding
aggregations of
hundreds of these fishes
swimming in mid-water
high above the bottom.
Photo of a 7-inch
individual by Dr. Gerald
R. Allen at Dixie Reef
(10 feet deep).

88.
Abudefduf
(*Glyphidodontops*)
rollandi (Whitley). This
pretty little damselfish
is only 2 inches long.
Photo by Dr. Gerald R.
Allen at One Tree Island
(8 feet deep).

89.
Abudefduf bengalensis
(Bloch). Australians
may record this species
under the name *A.
palmeri*. Photo by Dr.
Gerald R. Allen of a
6-inch individual at One
Tree Island (5 feet deep).

90.
Plectroglyphidodon johnstonianus Fowler and Ball. A shallow water species (less than 40 feet) usually associated with coral heads. Photo of a 4-inch individual from Flynn Reef by Dr. Gerald R. Allen (30 feet deep).

91.
Parma polylepis Gunther. This species is confined to the surge channels of the outer reef (Great Barrier Reef). Photo by Dr. Gerald R. Allen of a 4-inch individual at One Tree Island (6 feet deep).

92.
Abudefduf (Glyphidodontops) glaucus (Cuvier). Sombre damselfish. Occurring mainly on reef flats, this species feeds primarily on benthic algae. Photo of a 4-inch individual by Dr. Gerald R. Allen at One Tree Island (2 feet deep).

93.
Eupomacentrus gascoynei (Whitley). The range of this species is rather small, being found from northern New Zealand, New Caledonia, Lord Howe Island, and the southern tip of the Great Barrier Reef. Photo by Dr. Gerald R. Allen of a 4-inch individual from One Tree Island (10 feet deep).

94.
Eupomacentrus nigricans (Lacepede). Dusky demoiselle. This shallow water damselfish is encountered in lagoons and coastal reefs. Photo of a 6-inch individual by Dr. Gerald R. Allen at Opal Reef (20 feet deep).

95.
Paraglyphidodon polyacanthus (Ogilby). A colorful damselfish with almost the same distribution as the above *E. gascoynei*. Photo by Dr. Gerald R. Allen of a 4-inch fish from One Tree Island (20 feet deep).

96. *Paraglyphidodon polyacanthus* (Ogilby). The juvenile is almost entirely yellowish with the blue markings very evident. A larger specimen can be seen on the opposite page. Photo by Roger Steene.

97. *Paraglyphidodon melanopus* (Bleeker). This species is normally encountered in shallow water usually less than 10 feet deep and commonly around soft corals. Photo by Dr. Gerald R. Allen of a 3-inch individual from One Tree Island (6 feet deep).

98. *Paraglyphidodon polyacanthus* (Ogilby). As the cleaner (dark shadow in the foreground) makes its rounds, the fish remains still with its fins spread. Photo by Allan Power.

99.
Pomacentrus amboinensis Bleeker. Pallid damselfish. The color is quite variable and ranges from bright yellow to a pale purplish. Photo by Dr. Gerald Allen of a 3-inch fish from One Tree Island (20 feet deep).

100. *Pomacentrus amboinensis* Bleeker. The basic diet is algal although zooplankton is acceptable. Photo by Walter Deas at Wistari Reef (15 feet deep).

101.
Pomacentrus australis
Allen and Robertson.
This species has a very
limited distribution,
occurring from the
southern part of the
Great Barrier Reef to the
Sydney area. Photo by
Dr. Gerald R. Allen of a
3-inch individual from
Wistari Reef (30 feet
deep).

102. *Pomacentrus australis* Allen and Robertson. Individuals or small groups may be seen feeding on zooplankton above the bottom. Photo by Allan Power.

103.
Pomacentrus (Dischistodus) pseudochrysopoecilus Allen and Robertson. A shallow water species commonly found in lagoon reefs where there are patches of live coral. Photo by Dr. Gerald R. Allen of a 5-inch specimen from One Tree Island (6 feet deep).

104.
Pomacentrus wardi Whitley. Benthic algae form the basis of this fish's diet. It occurs in water less than 60 feet deep. Photo by Dr. Gerald R. Allen of a 3-inch fish from One Tree Island (6 feet deep).

105.
Pomacentrus (Dischistodus) notophthalmus (Bleeker). In one reference this species was called the yellow demoiselle, though this photo certainly does not show it as having much yellow. Photo of a 4-inch fish from One Tree Island by Dr. Gerald R. Allen.

106. *Pomacentrus (Dischistodus) pseudochrysopoecilus* Allen and Robertson. A younger version of the fish on the opposite page. This one shows the greater development of the white bars. Photo by Dr. Gerald R. Allen of a 3-inch fish from One Tree Island (5 feet deep).

107. *Pomacentrus (Dischistodus) prosopotaenia* Bleeker. A shallow water species that may be found in silty areas of lagoons and coastal reefs. Photo by Roger Steene.

108.
Pomacentrus melanochir Bleeker. This fish generally feeds on zooplankton a few feet off the bottom although benthic algae have also been found in the stomach contents. Photo by Dr. Gerald R. Allen of a 3-inch fish at One Tree Island (15 feet deep).

109. *Pomacentrus lepidogenys* Fowler and Bean. The range of this species is from the Philippines through Melanesia to the Great Barrier Reef. Photo of a 2-inch fish from Opal Reef by Dr. Gerald R. Allen (10 feet deep).

110.
Pomacentrus vaiuli
Jordan and Seale.
Young *P. vaiuli* are very
attractive and often
imported for the
aquarium trade. Photo
by Dr. Gerald R. Allen of
a 3-inch fish from
Wistari Reef (40 feet
deep).

111.
Pomacentrus pavo
(Bloch). Peacock
damselfish. A
widespread damselfish
that usually occurs in
small to large groups.
Photo by Dr. Gerald R.
Allen of a 4-inch fish
from One Tree Island
(15 feet deep).

112.
Pomacentrus flavicauda
Whitley. This is an algae
eater commonly found
in shallow water (1 to 10
feet) alone or in small
groups. Photo of a 3.5-
inch individual from One
Tree Island by Dr. Gerald
R. Allen.

113.
Acanthochromis polyacanthus (Bleeker). A common species found in many habitats. Its range includes the East Indies, Melanesia, the Philippines, and northern Australia. Photo of 6-inch adult with ½-1-inch young by Dr. Gerald R. Allen (Euston Reef, 20 feet deep).

114.
Pomacentrus lepidogenys Fowler and Bean. A zooplankton feeder that may occur as individuals or in groups. Photo by Dr. Gerald R. Allen of a 2-inch fish from Opal Reef.

115.
Pomacentrus philippinus Evermann and Seale. Only the Australian populations are entirely black like this. Those from other areas may have pale vertical fins. Photo by Dr. Gerald R. Allen of a 4-inch individual from Michaelmas Cay (15 feet deep).

116. *Pomacentrus azysron* Bleeker. The fish with the yellow tails are the damselfishes, those that are entirely blue are *Assessor*. Photo by Walter Deas at Heron Island (40 feet deep).

117. *Hologymnosus semidiscus* (Lacepede). Ringed wrasse. A relatively small individual which is starting to change over from juvenile to adult color. Photo of a 4-inch specimen from Spur Reef by Dr. Gerald R. Allen.

118. *Hologymnosus semidiscus* (Lacepede). A younger individual showing the juvenile pattern better. Photo by Roger Steene.

Family **LABRIDAE**
WRASSES

The wrasses of the family Labridae are well represented in Australian waters. More than a third of the genera have been reported from the Great Barrier Reef area, containing some 50 to 60 species. Most notable by its absence, or at least by its not being reported, is the bird wrasse genus *Gomphosus*. The largest genera as far as number of species is concerned are *Choerodon* and *Halichoeres*, both having 10 or more species on the Great Barrier Reef.

The genus *Choerodon*, or tusk fishes as they are commonly called in Australia, includes some of the largest wrasses, which reach lengths of four feet or more and weights of up to 40 pounds. They are compressed fishes with rather large scales. The dorsal fin is single and provided with 11 to 13 spines and about 7 rays. The snout is somewhat pointed with the upper head profile sloping. With age a fleshy hump develops on the head. The cheeks are deep and the jaws are provided with four strong canines (easily visible in some of the photos) which gave them the name of tusk fishes.

One of the aquarium favorites, the harlequin tusk fish or *Lienardella fasciata*, occurs in our area of coverage and apparently nowhere else in Australia. Recognition of this distinctive species is easier than trying to describe the anatomical differences between its genus and others of the family.

One of the more interesting genera of wrasses is *Epibulus*. Rather deep bodied and not particularly brightly colored, the unique feature of the single species of this genus is the highly protractile lower jaw. As the mouth is opened the entire lower part of the head seems to swing down and away, and the Australians have appropriately dubbed it the sling-jaw. The extended jaw creates an almost tube-like mouth.

The elongated *Hologymnosus semidiscus* is a wide-ranging species that apparently is not common on the Australian Great Barrier Reef. The juveniles are somewhat more colorful than the adult.

119. *Thalassoma lunare* (Linnaeus). Moon wrasse. Ascidians, sponges, corals, algae, etc. form the background for this excellent photo of the moon wrasse. Photo by Allan Power.

120.
Cirrhilabrus temmincki
Bleeker. This species
appears to extend from
Japan to Australia.
Photo by Roger Steene.

121. *Coris picta* (Bloch and Schneider). Comb-fish. This fish is more common south of Queensland but its range does extend to the Great Barrier Reef. Photo by Roger Steene.

122. *Lienardella fasciata* (Gunther). Harlequin tusk fish. Note how the enlarged upper and lower teeth fit together when the mouth is closed. Photo by Allan Power.

123.
Cheilinus undulatus Ruppell.
Hump-headed Maori wrasse. This specimen is only half grown at 3½ feet. Adults can grow to more than 7 feet long. Photo by Walter Deas.

124. *Achoerodus gouldii* (Richardson). Blue groper. The female has a different color pattern and is called the red groper. Photo by Ron Taylor.

125. *Cheilinus diagrammus* (Lacepede). Violet-lined Maori wrasse. This wide ranging species may grow to a foot and a half in length. Photo by Walter Deas at Heron Island (35 feet deep).

126. *Cheilinus diagrammus* (Lacepede). This species exhibits quite a bit of variation in color pattern as the various photos in this series of books show. Photo by Allan Power.

127.
Choerodon schoenleini (Valenciennes). Black-spot tusk fish. The black spot is the one in the dorsal fin; the tusk part of the common name refers to the canines in the front of the jaw. Photo by Allan Power.

128. *Choerodon schoenleini* (Valenciennes). The photographer caught this fish in an unusual pose. Even so, the fish has its eye trained toward the camera. Photo by Walter Deas at Heron Island (40 feet deep).

129. *Choerodon venustus* (De Vis). Venus tuskfish. A favorite of fishermen, this species is common around the coral reefs of the Capricorn group. Photo by Allan Power.

130. *Choerodon anchorago* (Bloch). Orange-dotted tusk fish. This species is widespread throughout the Indo-Pacific. It grows to a length of about one foot. Photo by Roger Steene.

131.
Bodianus axillaris
Bennett. Juvenile. These youngsters may be part-time cleaners, but most of their diet will be small invertebrate animals.
Photo by Allan Power.

132. *Bodianus loxozonus* (Snyder). Apparently *B. hirsutus* and *B. bilunulatus* are a different species, leaving this species with the name *loxozonus.* Photo by Allan Power.

133. *Bodianus axillaris* Bennett. Small fishes must be wary on the reef or they wind up as dinner for the larger fishes. Photo by Allan Power.

134. *Bodianus axillaris* Bennett. Invertebrates line the walls of caves and cover almost every square inch of space on the reef. Here the young *Bodianus* seems more intent on escape from the photographer than looking for its particular food animals. Photo by Dr. Gerald R. Allen of a 4-inch fish from Opal Reef.

135. *Stethojulis bandanensis* (Bleeker). Dotted rainbowfish. The common name comes from the dotted pattern of the female. This is the male. Photo by Roger Steene.

136. *Halichoeres trimaculatus* (Quoy and Gaimard). Spot-tail rainbowfish. Species of *Halichoeres* have specific patterns of color on the head. Photo by Roger Steene.

137. *Halichoeres centiquadrus* (Lacepede). A close up of the head is a very difficult underwater shot but was superbly executed in this photo. Photo by Allan Power.

138. *Hemigymnus melapterus* (Bloch). Black-eyed thick-lip. This individual is still in its subadult color pattern. It is only a few inches long as compared to the 3 feet of adult specimens. Photo by Allan Power.

139. *Thalassoma jansenii* (Bleeker). The pattern of this young fish is slightly different from the more adult specimen shown in Book 4 (p. 886). Photo by Roger Steene.

140. *Scarus niger* Forsskal. Dusky parrotfish. This species may be referred to in some texts as *Callyodon niger*. Photo by Walter Deas at Wilson Island (40 feet deep).

141. *Scarus ghobban* Forsskal. Blue-barred orange parrotfish. Additional photos of this species were presented in PMF Book 4 (pp. 990-992). Photo by Walter Deas.

142.
A parrotfish, probably
Scarus ghobban,
emerging from its
sleeping quarters,
possibly disturbed by
the photographer. Photo
by Walter Deas.

143. A graphic representation of the effects of parrotfishes nibbling on coral. The lighter areas in the coral are tooth (or beak) marks made by the parrots. Photo by Walter Deas at Heron Island (30 feet deep).

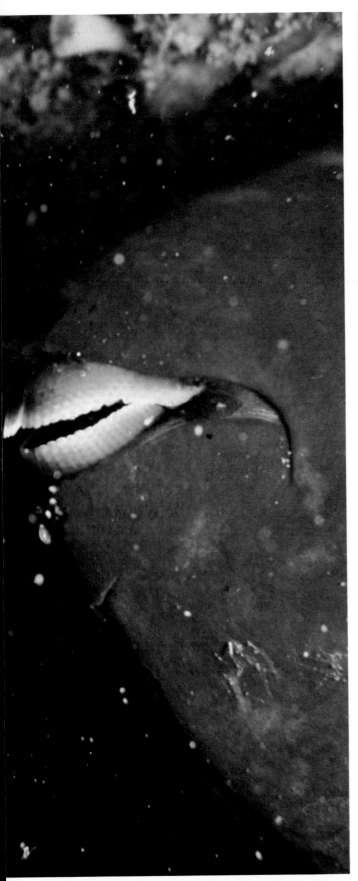

144. This is the business end of a parrotfish. showing the beak which is capable of making those marks on the opposite page. Photo by Walter Deas at Heron Island at night.

145. *Scarus frenatus* Lacepede. Pink parrotfish, No coral appears safe from these parrotfishes. Here a brain coral is being nibbled on by a pink parrotfish. This action is an important factor in reef erosion. Photo by Allan Power.

146. *Acanthurus dussumieri* Cuvier. Surgeonfishes browse on algae. This one is seen scraping some off what looks like dead coral. Photo by Walter Deas.

147. *Acanthurus dussumieri* Cuvier. The yellow markings around the eyes are shared by other species of *Acanthurus* but still provide aid in identification. Photo by Walter Deas at Heron Island (20 feet deep).

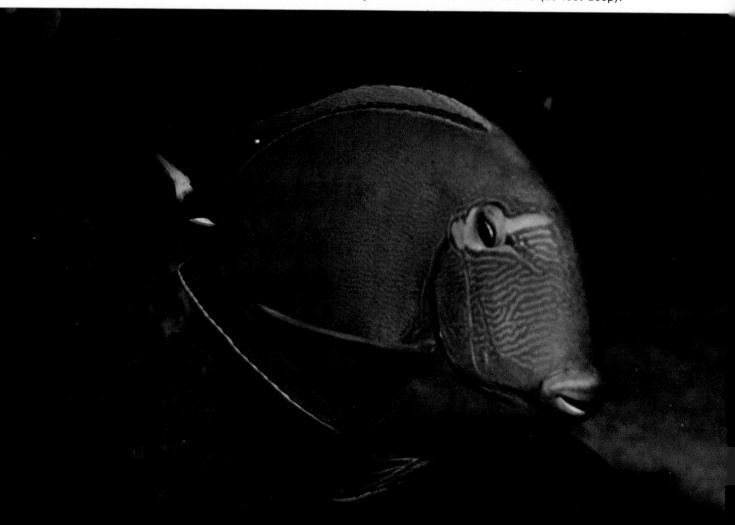

148. *Acanthurus mata* (Cuvier). Schools of surgeonfishes such as this one pass over the reef stopping now and then to graze. Photo by Dr. Gerald R. Allen (Great Barrier Reef, 30 feet deep).

149.
Acanthurus olivaceous
Bloch and Schneider.
Orange-spot surgeon-
fish. This photo of the
adult is included here for
comparison and may not
necessarily be of a
specimen from
Australia. Photo by
D. Terver, Nancy
Aquarium, France.

150. *Acanthurus olivaceous* Bloch and Schneider. This fish is probably about to change to the above coloration. Note the crescent-shaped caudal fin that develops with age. Photo by Roger Steene.

151. *Acanthurus glaucopareius* Cuvier. Note the short white dash under the eye as compared to the eye to snout band of the closely related *A. japonicus*. Photo by Dr. Gerald R. Allen of a 6-inch fish from Euston Reef (20 feet deep).

152. *Acanthurus lineatus* (Linnaeus). Blue-lined surgeonfish. The striped pattern of this fish makes it stand out from the rather drab background of coral rubble. Photo by Allan Power.

153. *Acanthurus bleekeri* Gunther. Pencilled surgeonfish. This species has been referred to as *A. bariene* at times, but that is an entirely different fish. Photo by Walter Deas, Wistari Reef (30 feet deep).

154. *Zebrasoma veliferum* (Bloch). Sail-finned surgeonfish. Juveniles do not venture far from a hiding place. They are also very fast and therefore difficult to catch. Photo by Allan Power.

155. *Zebrasoma scopas* (Cuvier). This sombre surgeonfish heads for cover, which in this instance happens to be a stand of staghorn coral. Note the white caudal spine. Photo by Walter Deas (Wistari Reef, 60 feet deep).

156. *Zanclus canescens* (Linnaeus). Moorish idol. A wide ranging species but reported to be rare in Queensland. Photo by Walter Deas.

157. *Zanclus canescens* (Linnaeus). Normally Moorish idols are encountered in pairs or small groups, rarely as individuals. Photo by Dr. Gerald R. Allen at Euston Reef (20 feet deep).

158. *Zanclus canescens* Linnaeus. There are a pair of small protuberances or horns above the eyes which can be seen in this photo. Photo by Allan Power.

159. *Siganus puellus* (Schlegel). Blue-lined spinefoot. Siganids generally browse on the coral reef in schools. Photo by Walter Deas at Heron Island.

Family SIGANIDAE
RABBITFISHES

Both genera of siganids, *Lo* and *Siganus*, are present in Australian waters. They are frequently found around the coral reef and rocky areas, sometimes in large schools. Many are quite colorful, with spots or stripes of golden yellow and blue.

The flesh is regarded as being quite good and they are often taken by fishermen on Queensland reefs. The fishermen have to beware of the poisonous spines when handling these fishes and have bestowed the common name 'stinging bream' upon them. The wound they inflict can be very painful and should be cared for as soon as possible.

The food is generally algae upon which they browse in much the manner of the related surgeonfishes. A school will move into an area of the reef and the fishes stop and nibble at the various growths, then moving on to greener pastures.

Rabbitfishes are said to spook easily and to try and take refuge wherever possible, including under a persons foot. This could be a problem if proper reef shoes are not worn for protection.

There are about a dozen species known from Queensland, all but one, *Lo vulpinus*, contained in the genus *Siganus*. They are difficult to differentiate for two reasons: the family is in need of revision and the species are now poorly defined, and they are quite variable, not only from one individual to the next but within the individual. There are various patterns associated with the moods of the fish, and a blotched fright or nighttime color may obscure the distinctive species pattern.

The Australians use the common name spinefoot for the various species, prefixing it with some descriptive word or words such as golden-lined, blue-spotted, blunt-nosed, or even coral. Of course local names are common and one reference gives a whole list of these for the black spinefoot (*Siganus rivulatus*), including such unusual ones as black trevally, Mi-Mi, happy moments, slimy, spiny, and stinging bream.

160. *Siganus virgatus* (Cuvier and Valenciennes). Juvenile. The double bar on the head helps to distinguish this species from *S. puellus*. Photo by Walter Deas at Heron Island (60 feet deep).

161.
Heniochus varius
(Cuvier). Horned
bullfish. This is another
species that has been
reported from
Queensland but is rare
there. Photo by Dr.
Gerald R. Allen (10 feet
deep).

162. *Heniochus varius* (Cuvier). The horns are well developed in this individual. Notice that the dorsal fin spines are not as well developed as in other species. Photo by Roger Steene.

163. *Heniochus chrysostomus* Cuvier. Three-banded bullfish. Like *H. varius*, this species is considered rare on the Great Barrier Reef. Photo by Walter Deas at Heron Island (50 feet deep).

164. *Heniochus acuminatus* (Linnaeus). Feather-fin bullfish. Notice the extremely long dorsal fin filament. This species and *Zanclus* can have filaments more than twice their body length. Photo by Allan Power. Wistari Reef (30 feet deep).

165. *Forcipiger flavissimus* Jordan and McGregor. Long-bill. One of the defensive reactions of butterflyfishes is to raise the dorsal fin spines. Photo by Walter Deas.

166. *Heniochus chrysostomus* Cuvier. Three-banded bullfish. The black pelvic fins blend in with the body band, the bright yellow pectoral fins stand out against it. Photo by Walter Deas.

167. *Heniochus acuminatus* (Linnaeus). This specie develops the typical horns very late, when the fish i already fully grown. Photo by Walter Deas.

168. *Forcipiger flavissimus* Jordan and McGregor. This is the common long-nosed butterflyfish, the one with the slightly shorter snout and wider mouth opening. Photo by Dr. Gerald R. Allen of a 5-inch fish from Euston Reef (30 feet deep).

169. *Forcipiger longirostris* Broussonet. This is the rarer species with a longer snout and smaller mouth opening. Photo by Dr. Gerald R. Allen of a 6-inch individual from Euston Reef (30 feet deep).

170.
Chelmon marginalis Richardson.
Young examples have a central
body stripe but this fades with age.
Photo by Walter Deas.

171. *Chelmon marginalis* Richardson. A slightly
older individual. Notice the ocellated spot
and body band are becoming weaker. Photo
by Allan Power.

172.
Chelmon rostratus
(Linnaeus). This species
differs in pattern from
C. marginalis. Note the
dark bordered body bar,
pelvic fins, more orange
color, etc. Photo by
Roger Steene. Great
Barrier Reef.

173. *Chelmon marginalis* Richardson. The adult has lost the body bar and the dorsal fin spot is well on the way out. Photo by Roger Steene. Great Barrier Reef.

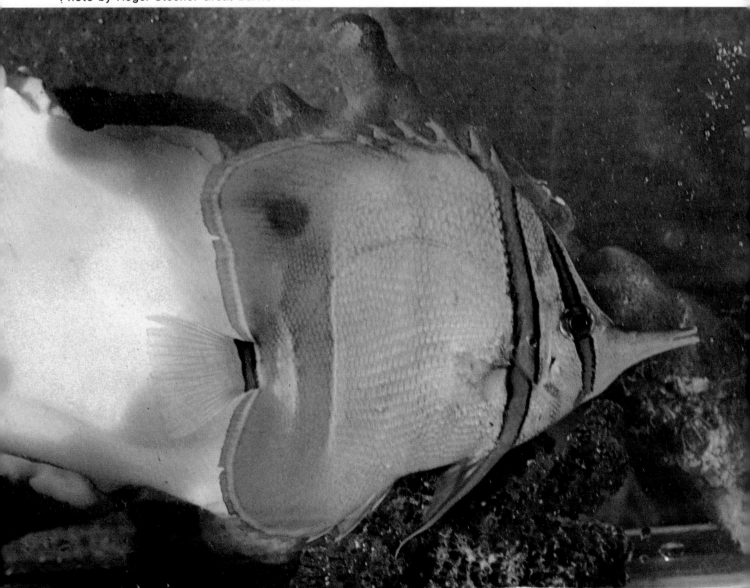

174.
Chelmon muelleri
Klunzinger. The
difference between this
species of *Chelmon* and
the others is fairly
obvious. Photo by
Roger Steene.

175. *Chelmon muelleri* Klunzinger. Blackfin coralfish. This species grows to a length of about 5-6 inches. Photo by Dr. Herbert R. Axelrod.

176. *Coradion altivelis* McCulloch. High-fin coralfish. The color pattern of *Coradion* species resembles that of the *Chelmon* species. Photo by Allan Power.

177. *Coradion altivelis* McCulloch. Typical of the coradions is the bifurcate body band. Photo by Walter Deas at Heron Island (35 feet deep).

178. *Chaetodon baronessa* Cuvier. A difficult species to keep in a home aquarium. Live coral is recommended as a supplement to its diet. Photo by Dr. Gerald R. Allen of a 5-inch individual from Euston Reef (30 feet deep).

179. *Chaetodon lineolatus* Cuvier. Lined butterflyfish. This unusual eye band pattern develops from a normal juvenile eye band. Photo by Walter Deas.

180. *Chaetodon lineolatus* Cuvier. Lined butterflyfish are usually found in pairs. The mate to this one is probably the fish under the nearby ledge. Photo of a 10-inch fish by Dr. Gerald R. Allen. Spur Reef (30 feet deep).

181. *Chaetodon mertensii* Cuvier. In Australia this fish has often been called *Chaetodon dixoni*. Photo by Dr. Gerald R. Allen at Jennie Louise Shoal (70 feet deep).

182. *Chaetodon vagabundus* Linnaeus. Criss-cross butterflyfish. A very common butterflyfish that grows to a length of about 8 inches. Photo by Dr. Gerald R. Allen, Great Barrier Reef (10 feet).

183. *Chaetodon unimaculatus* Bloch. A wide ranging species but not very common at any one locality. Photo by Walter Deas at Sykes Reef (30 feet deep).

184. *Chaetodon unimaculatus* Bloch. It is an accomplishment to get such a fine photo of this species of butterfly-fish. Normally the shy fish is heading for cover long before anyone can get this close. Photo by Dr. Gerald R. Allen at Euston Reef (30 feet deep).

185.
Chaetodon ephippium
Cuvier. Black-blotched
butterflyfish. This
species is not very
common in Australian
waters. Photo by
Walter Deas.

186. *Chaetodon trifascialis* Quoy and Gaimard. Right-angled butterflyfish. This species was first recorded from the Great Barrier Reef in 1946. Photo by Dr. Gerald R. Allen at Euston Reef (30 feet deep).

187.
Chaetodon auriga
Forsskal. Threadfin
butterflyfish. A common
wide ranging species
found on the Great
Barrier Reef and
extending south into
northern New South
Wales. Photo by Walter
Deas.

188. *Chaetodon semeion* Bleeker. The dark area on the side of the fish here is a fright reaction, probably due to the confinement necessary to photograph it. Photo by Roger Steene.

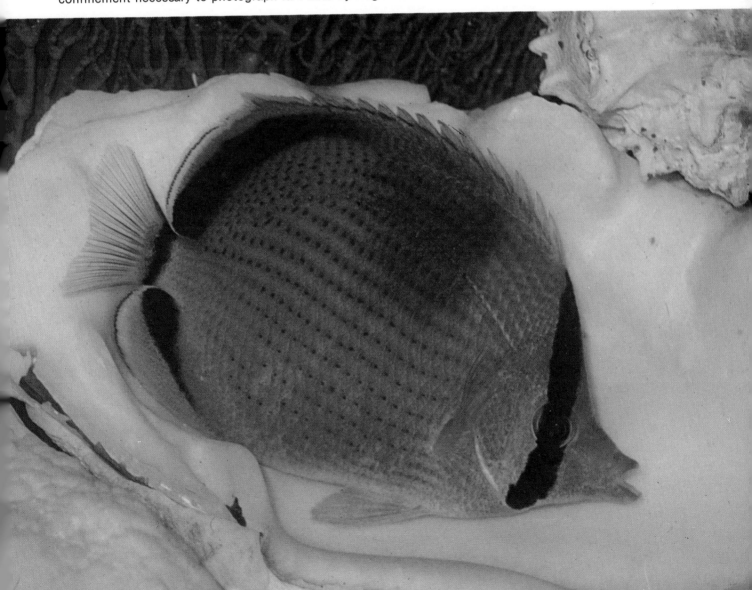

189. *Chaetodon pelewensis* Kner. Dot-and-dash butterflyfish. The lateral pattern in this individual has become muddled. Photo of a 4-inch individual by Dr. Gerald R. Allen at Euston Reef (30 feet deep).

190. *Chaetodon pelewensis* Kner. A more normal pattern but still with some extraneous bifurcations. Photo by Roger Steene.

191. *Chaetodon pelewensis* Kner. The typical color pattern. This fish is moving in on some juicy tidbit on the reef. Photo by Walter Deas.

192. *Chaetodon plebeius* Cuvier. Blue-blotched butterflyfish. A rather common butterflyfish on the Great Barrier Reef. which is said to be rarer elsewhere. Photo by Keith Gillett.

193. *Chaetodon plebeius* Cuvier. In captivity this species requires live foods, particularly live coral, to be at its best. Photo by Dr. Gerald R. Allen of a 4-inch fish at One Tree Island (6 feet deep).

194. *Chaetodon guentheri* Ahl. The dark dorsal fin spot is very weak in this individual. This species extends its range up to southern Japan. Photo by Roger Steene.

195. *Chaetodon speculum* Cuvier. A common, fairly hardy butterflyfish that is imported from time to time for the aquarium trade. Photo by Dr. Gerald R. Allen of a 4-inch fish at One Tree Island.

196. *Chaetodon citrinellus* Cuvier. Speckled butterflyfish. This species is quite common in Queensland but its numbers decrease rapidly southward. Photo by Dr. Gerald R. Allen at Kenn Reef (20 feet deep).

197. *Chaetodon trifasciatus* Park. Lineated butterflyfish. Although quite common elsewhere in its range, this fish is said to be uncommon in Queensland waters. Photo by Allan Power.

198. *Chaetodon trifasciatus* Park. A coral feeder that rarely does well in captivity. Photo by Dr. Gerald R. Allen at Euston Reef (30 feet deep).

199. Butterflyfishes and damselfishes swim about the coral (*Acropora*) at a depth of about 30 feet. Seen are *Chaeto-don kleinii* and *Chaetodon aureofasciatus*. Photo by Walter Deas at Wistari Reef (30 feet deep).

200. *Chaetodon rainfordi* McCulloch. Rainford's butterflyfish. This juvenile butterflyfish will attain a size of about 6 inches when fully grown. Photo by Allan Power.

201. *Chaetodon rainfordi* McCulloch. An adult keeping a wary eye on the photographer. Photo by Walter Deas at Heron Island (60 feet deep).

202.
Chaetodon rainfordi
McCulloch. This species
has a fairly restricted
range. It is found only
on the Queensland
coast. Photo by Roger
Steene.

203. A look at the domain of this butterflyfish at North-West Island, Capricorn Group. Photo by Allan Power.

204. *Chaetodon rainfordi* McCulloch. Adult. The sharp dorsal spines are raised for more protection, but the best defense of butterflyfishes is flight. Photo by Allan Power.

206. *Chaetodon aureofasciatus* Macleay. Golden-striped butterflyfish. The body banding is absent in this species but the head pattern is very similar to *C. rainfordi*. Photo by Walter Deas, Heron Island.

205. *Chaetodon rainfordi* McCulloch. Compare this species with the following one. They are very closely related. Photo by Allan Power.

207. *Chaetodon aureofasciatus* Macleay. Very few of these fishes are imported into the United States. When they are the price is relatively high. Photo by Roger Steene.

208. *Chaetodon aureofasciatus* Macleay. The range of this butterflyfish is not great, but it is not as small as that of *C. rainfordi*. Photo by Dr. Gerald R. Allen of a 5-inch individual from Michaelmas Cay.

209. *Chaetodon aureofasciatus* Macleay. This species attains a length of about 6 inches when fully grown. Photo by Allan Power.

210. *Chaetodon flavirostris* Gunther. Dusky butterflyfish. This species is not common on the Queensland coast. Photo by Walter Deas at Heron Island.

211. *Chaetodon flavirostris* Gunther. The adult is generally dark in color except for some orange and yellow in the head and fins. Photo by Walter Deas at Heron Island (20 feet deep).

212. *Chaetodon flavirostris* Gunther. The light patch below the dorsal fin is part of the normal coloration of this fish. Photo by Walter Deas at Heron Island (40 feet deep).

213. *Chaetodon flavirostris* Gunther. This individual is somewhat intermediate in color between the juvenile and adult. Photo by Dr. Gerald R. Allen at One Tree Island (6 feet deep).

214. A look at Spur Reef, Great Barrier Reef, at a depth of about 20 feet. Note the *Chaetodon ornatissimus* adult in the foreground. Photo by Dr. Gerald R. Allen.

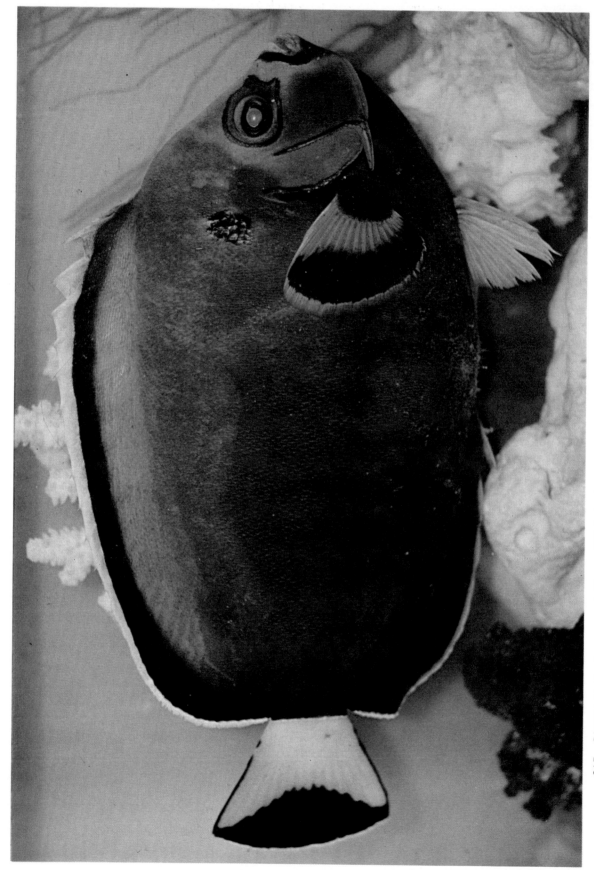

215. *Chaetodontoplus conspicillatus* (Waite). Spectacled angelfish. A distinctive angelfish found on the Great Barrier Reef and Lord Howe Island. Photo by Roger Steene.

216. *Chaetodontoplus duboulayi* (Gunther). Scribbled angelfish. This beautiful angelfish has been imported into the United States from time to time. The vermiculations on its side have earned it its common name. Photo by Dr. Herbert R. Axelrod.

217. *Chaetodontoplus duboulayi* (Gunther). This individual does not show the characteristic scribbled pattern. Photo by Roger Steene.

218.
*Chaetodontoplus
personifer* (McCulloch).
Spotted-face angelfish.
Note the difference in
head pattern between
this individual and those
in the other photos.
Photo by Walter Deas.

219. *Chaetodontoplus personifer* (McCulloch). The broad white band on the head may be sexually dimorphic. The caudal fin should also be yellow but may simply be in a shadow. Photo by Allan Power.

220. *Chaetodontoplus personifer* (McCulloch). A close-up of the fantastic head pattern of this angelfish. Photo by Walter Deas at Heron Island (35 feet deep).

221. *Chaetodontoplus personifer* (McCulloch). The caudal fin pattern differs from the Taiwan specimens illustrated in PMF-5 (pp. 1121-23). Considering the variability of the color pattern in other species of this genus, no great significance can be attached to this observation at this time. Photo by Roger Steene.

222. *Pomacanthus semicirculatus* (Cuvier and Valenciennes). Zebra angelfish. This is one of the large common angelfishes found in the Indo-Pacific region. Photo by Allan Power.

223. *Pomacanthus semicirculatus* (Cuvier and Valenciennes). A subadult with traces of the blue lines of the juvenile. Photo by Walter Deas at Heron Island (40 feet deep).

224.
Pomacanthus semicirculatus (Cuvier and Valenciennes). The cleaner wrasse, *Labroides dimidiatus*, is allowed to pick around the gills even though it is a very delicate area. Many fishes have parasites in the gill area that must be removed. Photo by Allan Power.

225. *Pomacanthus semicirculatus* (Cuvier and Valenciennes). Corals and other invertebrate animals form part of the diet of angelfishes. This one may be about to nip at some polyps of a coelenterate. Photo by Walter Deas.

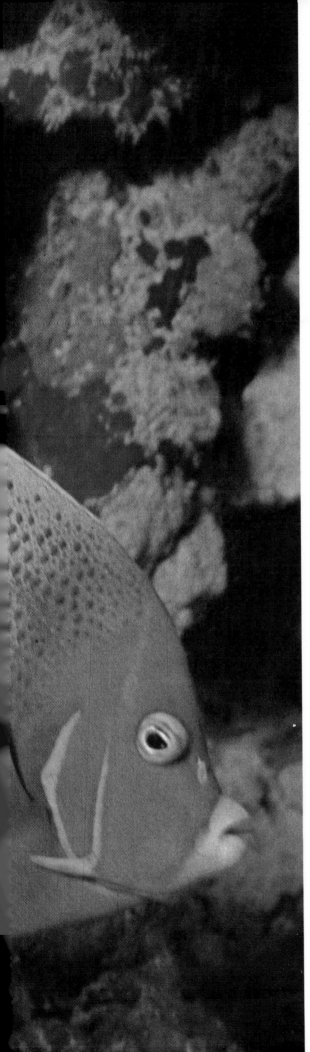

226.
Pomacanthus semicirculatus (Cuvier and Valenciennes). Although not as brightly colored as many of the other species of angelfishes, this one is quite pretty. Photo by Allan Power.

227. *Pomacanthus semicirculatus* (Cuvier and Valenciennes). Most angelfishes are not shy if approached carefully, but this one still keeps a wary eye on the photographer. Photo by Allan Power.

228. *Pomacanthus semicirculatus* (Cuvier and Valenciennes). Few photographers can get such detail in an underwater photo. The teeth, scales, nostrils, etc. are all easily discernible. Photo by Walter Deas at Heron Island at night (30 feet deep).

229. *Pomacanthus semicirculatus* (Cuvier and Valenciennes). This species gets quite large, individuals of 15 inches being reported. Photo by Walter Deas at Heron Island (30 feet deep).

230.
Euxiphipops sexstriatus (Cuvier and Valenciennes). Six-banded angelfish. Another common angelfish found in Australia that grows to a large size, 20 inches or more. Photo by Allan Power at Sykes Reef (15 feet deep).

231. *Pomacanthus imperator* (Bloch). Emperor angelfish. The emperor or imperial angelfish is less common in Queensland waters than the previous two species. Photo by Allan Power at Sykes Reef (30 feet deep).

232. *Pomacanthus imperator* (Bloch). A coral reef is a rugged area providing many hiding places even for fishes as large as this emperor angelfish. Note the lack of the dorsal fin filament. Photo by Dr. Gerald R. Allen of a 12-inch individual at Spur Reef (30 feet deep).

233. *Pygoplites diacanthus* (Boddaert). Regal angelfish. The sharp preopercular spine is blue in color, making it very conspicuous in this photo. Photo by Allan Power at Wistari Reef (60 feet deep).

234. An overhanging coral ledge provides shelter for this regal angelfish (*Pygoplites diacanthus*) and butterflyfish (*Coradion altivelis*). Photo by Walter Deas.

235. *Pygoplites diacanthus* (Boddaert). This regal angelfish is retiring to the safety of the sharp coral (*Acropora*). Photo by Dr. Gerald R. Allen of a 7-inch fish from Euston Reef.

236. *Genicanthus melanospilus* (Bleeker). A male (below) and female (above) striped angelfish. The black caudal bands are highly variable and may be present or absent depending upon the individual. Photo by Roger Steene.

237. *Euxiphipops sexstriatus* (Cuvier and Valenciennes). The pelvic fins are extremely long in this species of angelfish. Photo by Walter Deas at Heron Island.

Family AULOSTOMIDAE
TRUMPETFISHES

Aulostomus chinensis, the common trumpetfish, inhabits the tropical reefs of Australia including the Great Barrier Reef. It is known there by at least two common names, the spiny-back trumpetfish, referring of course to the 8-12 isolated dorsal fin spines, and the painted flutemouth, which could refer to the bright yellow phase shown on these pages or one of the other color patterns often exhibited by this species.

They are predators, normally inhabiting shallow waters where they are often seen by divers. Mention has been made before of the behavior of this fish wherein it will lie alongside or just above a larger fish as it moves about the reef. It is also said to adopt this pose in relation to a diver, lying alongside his back out of sight.

In some places where gorgonians grow this fish will lie head down among them,

238. *Aulostomus chinensis* (Linnaeus). Spiny-back trumpetfish. The snout is very compressed but the jaws open relatively wide to engulf prey animals. Note the barbel at the symphysis of the lower jaw. Photo by Walter Deas at Heron Island.

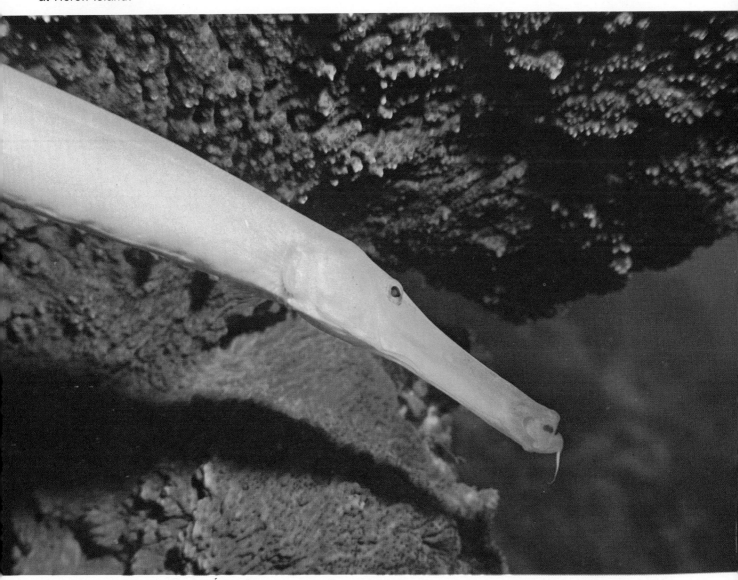

drifting back and forth in the current as they do and assuming a color which makes them very difficult to spot. In Australia the cover used is usually coral branches, mostly *Acropora* (a branching coral), and the gorgonian wire weed.

It is very easily identified by its form and not likely to be confused with any other reef fish. Even the flutemouth, *Fistularia petimba*, which is also elongate, is distinctive enough so that there would be no confusion between the two.

Regardless of its predatory habitat, however, this fish will also allow the small cleaner wrasse, *Labroides*, to investigate its body in search of parasites.

The small fins should not delude one into thinking this is a slow fish. It can dart out of its hiding place very rapidly in order to grab a passing fish.

239.
Aulostomus chinensis (Linnaeus). This fish may turn rather suddenly to a brown or striped phase. It also goes by the name of painted flutemouth. Photo by Walter Deas.

240. *Aulostomus chinensis* (Linnaeus) and *Lab-roides dimidiatus* (Cuvier and Valenciennes). Even a fish eater like the trumpetfish stands still to be cleaned. Sometimes more than one cleaner will take part in the search for parasites. Photo by Allan Power.

241.
Aulostomus chinensis
(Linnaeus) and
Epinephelus areolatus
(Forsskal). The spiny-
back trumpetfish will lie
along the back of a
larger fish then dash out
to capture a small one as
it comes too close.
Photo by Walter Deas.

242. *Aulostomus chinensis* (Linnaeus). Although a rather odd looking and interesting fish, this species is very seldom kept in home aquaria. Photo by Allan Power at Wistari Reef (50 feet deep).

Family ECHENEIDAE
REMORAS AND SUCKERFISHES

Remoras are very unusual fishes. They are slender, elongate, and range in size up to about three feet. What sets them apart from most other fishes is the modification of the first dorsal fin. The spines of this fin are deflected alternately to the right and left, lying flat against the fish and the whole thing is surrounded by a ridge forming a complete disc. The remoras can, by means of this structure, attach themselves to almost any large object, the modified spines or plates creating a number of vacuum chambers. These plates are inclined posteriorly so that if the remora is grabbed by the tail and pulled backward the grip becomes tighter. The suction is so powerful that, if the fish did not let go under a severe pull, it could be literally pulled apart. To remove a remora, if it is inclined to remain attached, try pushing it forward with the grain so to speak. The most common objects of attachment are large fishes, preferably sharks, but marlin, turtles, large groupers, sunfishes, mantas or devil rays, and at times small boats or ships are often used. Native fishermen have been known to fish with remoras, tying a line to their tails and letting them search out a large fish or turtle for attachment. Once attached, the remora is retrieved with the line, still holding on to its "host".

The remoras thus get a free ride, which the host fish does not seem to mind, and possibly a free meal as the larger fish sloppily dines on some other fish. The remoras may not only dine on the scraps of the larger fishes, but may also eat some of the parasites that become attached to it. Actually, the remoras are good swimmers and can fare quite well by themselves. They are able to change position while riding on the host as it is swimming rapidly.

243. *Echeneis naucrates* Linnaeus. Slender sucking-fish. As a large fish is hauled aboard, the *Echeneis* will attach itself to anything handy, including the bottom of the boat. Photo by Allan Power.

244. *Echeneis naucrates* Linnaeus. A good view of the entire fish. It is rare to see these fishes swimming about freely. Photo by D. Terver, Nancy Aquarium, France.

245. *Echeneis naucrates* (Linnaeus). A close up of the modified dorsal fin. Each dorsal fin spine was altered into one of the ridges. Photo by Dr. Herbert R. Axelrod.

246. *Makaira* sp. One of the big game fishes of the Queensland coast. It inhabits the open ocean waters and is generally caught trolling. Underwater photographs of this type of fish are rare. Photo by Walter Deas.

247. *Seriola grandis* Castelnau. King amberjack. This schooling fish grows to a length of 6 feet and a weight of 150 pounds. Photo by Allan Power.

248.
Caranx sp. This species was identified as *C. ignobilis*, the silver trevally, but without specimens the identification is tentative. Photo by Allan Power.

249.
Caranx emburyi
(Whitley). Turrum. This
species is considered a
fine game fish in
Australia around the
Queensland coast.
Photo by Allan Power.

250. *Caranx melampygus* Cuvier. Blue-finned trevally. This colorful carangid attains a length of over two feet. Photo by Allan Power.

251. ?*Caranx fulvoguttatus* (Forsskal). Gold-spotted trevally. A reef inhabiting carangid that grows to a length of about three feet. Photo by Allan Power.

252. *?Caranx ferdau* (Forsskal). Yellow-spotted trevally. The lateral line is very low in this species, almost straight. The spots on the sides would appear yellow in the proper light. Photo by Walter Deas at Kenn Reef (40 feet deep).

253. *Caranx* sp. A school of carangids in the barred phase. These bars come and go according to the mood of the fish. Photo by Walter Deas at Heron Island.

254. *Parapercis cylindrica* (Bloch). Sharp-nosed weever. This species is often found in sandy areas propped up on its ventral fins. Photo by Allan Power.

255. *Parapercis cylindrica* (Bloch). When danger threatens it seeks shelter under nearby rock or coral ledges. Photo by Allan Power.

256. *Goniistius fuscus* (Richardson). Red morwong. Individuals occur in the southern part of the Barrier Reef and throughout New South Wales where it is more common. Photo by Walter Deas.

257. *Goniistius gibbosus* (Richardson). Magpie morwongs. It has been reported that individuals of this species may be so unafraid of a diver that they follow him about. Photo by Walter Deas.

258. *Goniistius gibbosus* (Richardson). A close up photo showing the characteristic markings on the head and anterior part of the body. Photo by Dr. Herbert R. Axelrod.

259.
Platax batavianus
(Cuvier). Hump-headed
batfish. Old individuals
develop a large
protruding forehead,
hence the common
name. Photo by Walter
Deas.

260. *Platax pinnatus* (Linnaeus). Batfish. Adults do not have the greatly elongate fins of the juveniles. The protruding snout helps identify the adult of this species. Photo by Dr. Gerald R. Allen of 15-18-inch individuals at Euston Reef (30 feet deep).

261. *Platax teira* (Forsskal). Young batfishes are relatively easy to identify; adults are difficult and tooth and fin structures are needed for positive identification. Photo by Walter Deas.

262. *Platax* sp. (possibly *P. batavianus*). Old individuals get a characteristic hump above the snout. Photo by Allan Power.

263. A school of small fishes, probably pempherids. They are rendered more visible by the photographic flash. Photo by Walter Deas.

264. A school of what appears to be the common hardyhead, *Pranesus ogilbyi* Whitley. Large shoals of this fish may be found in shallow bays and estuaries over sandy areas. Photo by Allan Power.

265. A compound school of clupeids, composed of at least two species. The lower, deeper bodied one may be a species of *Hyperlophus*, the upper, more slender bodied fish must remain unidentified. Notice the two species heading in opposite directions and the sharp edge to the school. Photo by Allan Power.

266. *Pardachirus pavoninus* Lacepede. Peacock sole. The color and pattern of this sole match the sandy background quite well. The eyes and mouth are particularly difficult to distinguish in this individual. Photo by Allan Power.

267. ?*Thysanophrys cirronasus* (Richardson). Rock flathead. This species is more common in New South Wales but does occur in the southern Great Barrier Reef area. Photo by Allan Power.

268. *Cirrhitichthys aprinus* (Cuvier). Blotched hawkfish. Hawkfishes commonly rest quietly on coral heads or sponges. However, they can move very quickly when darting after prey or fleeing from danger. Photo by Walter Deas, Heron Island (45 feet deep).

269. *Cirrhitichthys aprinus* (Cuvier). The barred pattern has been broken up into large blotches in this individual. Photo by Walter Deas.

270. *Cirrhitichthys aprinus* (Cuvier). The thickened lower pectoral fin rays and the fringes of the dorsal fin spines are clearly visible in this photograph. Photo by Walter Deas.

271. *Cirrhitichthys falco* Randall. Notice how similar the pattern of this hawkfish is to the previous species. Photo by Allan Power.

272. *Paracirrhites forsteri* (Schneider). Freckled hawkfish. Hawkfishes have been reported as relatively uncommon in Queensland waters. Our photographers seem to have no trouble finding them. Photo by Allan Power.

273. *Paracirrhites arcatus* (Cuvier). Ring-eyed hawkfish. This fish has appeared under another name, *Gymnocirrhites arcatus*, but we are using the most widely accepted name. Photo by Allan Power.

Family BATRACHOIDIDAE
TOADFISHES AND MIDSHIPMEN

Toadfishes are bottom-dwelling fishes that occur in temperate and tropical seas. They are found at various depths from the shore line to the edge of the continental shelf, with a few species able to penetrate brackish waters of estuaries and even pure fresh water. They can withstand the dry periods of low tide and often can be seen moving slowly over the mud flats after the tide has receded. They are good burrowers and commonly remain hidden in the mud with only part of their head exposed, either in the water or out of it (they may disappear into the mud if approached). It is possible that they can use the oral and supraciliary tentacles as lures in much the same manner as the frog- or anglerfishes. Aside from the mud bottom, the slow swimming toadfishes are found in grass flats, apparently where they also blend in with the background so as to remain undetected by the prey. In many instances the water in which they remain may become so oxygen deficient that other fishes may be killed, the toadfishes however being able to tolerate such conditions, at least for a limited time. Some species make spawning migrations from deep water to very shallow water.

The eggs are large and relatively few in number (50 to 75 being found in some species) and may be laid attached to various solid objects such as rocks, old tin cans, old shoes, and other debris. The male is said to guard the eggs for the time which it takes them to hatch (about 10 days to a month). At breeding time the toadfishes are said to be quite nasty and will bite at the slightest provocation. They have large mouths and strong jaws that can crush mollusc or crustacean shells as well as a person's fingers or toes (if he be so unlucky as to step on one).

Some of the toadfishes (though apparently none from Queensland waters) have poison sacs associated with the dorsal fin spines and gill cover spines. These spines are hollow and act like hypodermic needles as they puncture the skin of an unwary fish or person. The Queensland toadfishes do have a mucus which is toxic (or at least causes discomfort and probably infection of a wound).

274. ?*Halophryne diemensis* (Lesueur). Banded frogfish. A fairly common fish occurring from tropical Australia through the East Indies to India. Photo by Allan Power.

275.
Scorpaenopsis cirrhosa
(Thunberg). Few
scorpionfishes have
such well developed cirri
on the chin. These,
along with the spine
pattern of the head, help
identify this species.
Photo by Allan Power.

276. *Scorpaena* sp. The well-developed cirri are on the upper jaw in this species. It was identified for us by one authority as *S. neglecta* Temminck and Schlegel. Photo by Jean Deas.

277.
?Paracentropogon vespa
(Ogilby). Freckled wasp-
fish. A poorly known
species usually trawled
in water 7 to 13 fathoms
deep. Photo by Walter
Deas.

278. *Scorpaena* sp. The same species as represented on the opposite page. There is no well developed supraorbital tentacle in this species. Photo by Allan Power.

279. *Scorpaenopsis cirrhosa* (Thunberg). The large mouth can easily engulf small fishes. If you keep scorpaenids in an aquarium, be sure not to put small fishes in with them unless they are intended as food. Photo by Allan Power.

280.
Synanceia verrucosa
Bloch and Schneider.
Stonefish. The
sculpturing of the head
of the stonefish makes it
look quite ominous. In
this case the devil-like
look is backed up by
some highly poisonous
spines. Photo by Walter
Deas at Yeppoon,
Queensland.

281. *Synanceia verrucosa* Bloch and Schneider. The strong dorsal spines (one is partly exposed here) are provided with venom sacs and can penetrate a thin-soled shoe. Photo by Allan Power.

282. *Synanceia verrucosa* Bloch and Schneider. It would be difficult to distinguish this fish from encrusted rocks, some of which can be seen in this photo. Photo by Allan Power.

283. *Dendrochirus zebra* (Cuvier and Valenciennes). Zebra firefish. Apparently only occasionally encountered on the Great Barrier Reef, this fish is most common in the northern section. Photo by Allan Power.

284.
Pterois volitans
Linnaeus. Red firefish.
This species is
widespread in the Indo-
Pacific and occurs
throughout the Great
Barrier Reef. Photo by
Walter Deas.

285. *Dendrochirus brachypterus* (Cuvier and Valenciennes). The two common species of *Dendrochirus* can easily be distinguished. Note the differences between this individual and that of the other species on the opposite page. Photo by Roger Steene.

286.
Pterois antennata
(Bloch). Butterfly cod.
When seen these fishes
almost always have their
fins spread. Only when
they are swimming fast
do they fold the large
pectorals back to reduce
drag. Photo by Allan
Power.

287. *Dendrochirus zebra* (Cuvier and Valenciennes). This popular aquarium fish has accumulated several common names in the Australia-New Guinea area alone. A few are dwarf lionfish, zebra butterfly-cod, and of course the most commonly used, zebra firefish. Photo by Keith Gillett.

288.
Pterois antennata
(Bloch). Spotfin
lionfish. Another fish
with several common
names. This one is also
called the rough-scaled
turkeyfish and the
ragged-finned butterfly-
cod. Photo by Walter
Deas.

289. *Pterois antennata* (Bloch). The supraorbital tentacles are spectacularly developed in this fish. Photo by Roger Steene.

290. *Pterois antennata* (Bloch). The patterns of the lionfishes make them very conspicuous on a drab background like this one. The white spot at the base of the pectoral fin is always present. Photo by Allan Power.

291. *Pterois volitans* Linnaeus. One of the lighter phases of lionfishes sitting on top of some soft coral. Photo by Walter Deas at the northern edge of Heron Island.

292. *Pterois volitans* Linnaeus. The dark phase of this species. Notice that the long pectoral rays are almost solid blackish brown. Photo by Walter Deas at Heron Island.

293. *Pterois lunulata* Temminck and Schlegel. Large lionfishes can be quite spectacular in an aquarium. They grow to about one foot in length. Photo by Walter Deas at Heron Island (60 feet deep).

294. *Pterois volitans* Linnaeus. Lionfishes are sometimes called featherfins. Note the well developed cirri on the upper jaw. Photo by Walter Deas.

295. The fish in this photo is a problem. It was identified for us as *Malacanthus latovittatus* and may be the first photo of the young stage. Note the resemblance also to juvenile *Hologymnosus semidiscus*. Photo by Dr. Gerald R. Allen of a 5-inch individual.

296. *Kyphosus cinerascens* (Forsskal). Topsail drummer. A relatively common fish found along the Queensland coast. It grows to about 18 inches and is utilized as a food fish. Photo by Allan Power.

297.
Diploprion bifasciatum
Cuvier. This is the same
species as that below
and opposite, but a
color variety. It is not
common and rarely if
ever appears for sale in
aquarium stores. Photo
by Roger Steene.

298. *Diploprion bifasciatum* Cuvier. Yellow emperor. A not too common species on the Great Barrier Reef, this species grows to a length of about one foot. Photo by Walter Deas at Heron Island (60 feet deep).

299. *Diploprion bifasciatum* Cuvier. The more normal coloration of the yellow emperor. The posterior band may become more sharply defined in some individuals. Photo by Walter Deas.

300. *Diploprion bifasciatum* Cuvier. Another common name for this species has been two-banded perch. It has been placed in a family by itself by some workers. Photo by Dr. Gerald R. Allen of an 8-inch individual at Euston Reef (30 feet deep).

301. *Plectropomus maculatus* (Bloch). Coral trout or leopard-fish. This is a highly variable species as this and the following pages will show. Some ichthyologists have accepted as many as three species in this genus. Photo by Walter Deas at Heron Island (40 feet deep).

Family SERRANIDAE
GROUPERS

Groupers are well represented on the Great Barrier Reef but are known by names quite different from the ones we are most used to. The groupers, or gropers, or garrupas are referred to in general as rock cods, with more specific names for each species such as freckled rock cod, blue-spotted rock cod, flag-tailed rock cod, etc.

One of the better known species is the coral cod, *Cephalopholis miniatus*. It is strikingly colored as the photos on these pages show. The bright red color easily distinguishes it from other groupers, even the coral trout, *Plectropomus maculatus,* which also has a red phase but with the red much more subdued. In addition, the caudal fin of the coral trout is truncate or squarish when compared to that of the coral cod, and there are nine dorsal spines in *Cephalopholis miniatus* and only seven or eight in *Plectropomus.*

The coral cod is relatively common on the Great Barrier Reef but is quite shy, hiding during the day under ledges or in caves. Although it has what seems to be an insatiable appetite, it is not often caught by fishermen, perhaps due to its secretive behavior. When it is caught it is a good table fish, adults running from about 5½ to 8 pounds and reaching a length of up to 18 inches. Its diet appears to consist of a combination of fishes and crustaceans.

The most common genus of groupers in Queensland waters is *Epinephelus* with over a dozen species. Most are sombre-colored fishes with browns dominating. One of the more recognizable groupers is the wire-netting cod or honeycomb rock cod, *Epinephelus merra*. This moderate-sized species (it reaches a length of about

302. *Plectropomus maculatus* (Bloch). This individual has come to a cleaning station manned by a *Labroides dimidiatus* which is searching the head area for parasites. Photo by Walter Deas at Heron Island (25 feet deep).

303. *Plectropomus maculatus* (Bloch). A distinctly different color pattern of the same species. There are several blue dots still visible, however. This fish is in what is called the "tiger" phase in Australia. Photo by Walter Deas.

18 inches) has a pattern of hexagonal spots separated by light lines. It also seeks shelter under ledges or in caves, though in deeper water it is said to spend some time in the open on a broken bottom (though not far from some shelter). Its principal diet consists of fish and shellfish. In shallower water smaller individuals may be found by turning over dead coral slabs at low tide.

The estuary rock cod or greasy cod, *Epinephelus tauvina*, is one of the largest groupers in Queensland waters, reportedly attaining lengths of up to seven feet and a weight of 500 pounds. It is found commonly on the inshore and offshore reefs as well as in the brackish water of estuaries along the Queensland coast. It finds refuge amid the coral and weeds or around piers or wrecks where it feeds on fish and crustaceans.

304. *Plectropomus maculatus* (Bloch). A large coral cod cruising around the reef. Very few predators could tackle a full-sized four-foot individual. Photo by Allan Power.

305. *Plectropomus maculatus* (Bloch). This individual was apparently caught by the camera between the gray-blue and red color phases. Photo by Walter Deas.

306. *Plectropomus maculatus* (Bloch). The red or leopard phase. This species can be caught by trolling, an unusual occurrence with bottom types like groupers. Photo by Allan Power.

307. *Cephalopholis urodelus* (Bloch and Schneider). Flag-tailed rock cod. This species is reported to be rare on the Queensland coast. Here an individual was spotted over some *Acropora* coral. Photo by Dr. Gerald R. Allen at Euston Reef (20 feet deep).

308. *Cephalopholis urodelus* (Bloch and Schneider). Typically grouper-shaped, this species reaches only about 10 inches in length. Photo by Allan Power.

309. *Plectropomus maculatus* (Bloch). A close up of the head showing the eye pattern and some of the blue spots. Photo by Walter Deas at Heron Island (30 feet deep).

310.
Cephalopholis miniatus
(Forsskal). Coral trout.
A colorful species
common on the
Queensland coast but
not further south. Photo
by Walter Deas.

311. *Cephalopholis miniatus* (Forsskal). The eyes can swivel independently in their sockets. This grouper is keeping at least one eye on the photographer. Photo by Allan Power.

312. *Cephalopholis miniatus* (Forsskal). When a fish poses this nicely it probably means a cleaner wrasse is close by. There appears to be one near the rocks below the fish. Photo by Allan Power.

313. *Epinephelus tauvina* (Forsskal). This grouper is being cleaned by what appears to be a *Bodianus axillaris* juvenile. Unfortunately at this angle it is difficult to determine with certainty. Photo by Walter Deas at Heron Island (60 feet deep).

314. *Epinephelus tauvina* (Forsskal). Estuary rock cod. This species gets very large, reaching a length of 7 feet and a weight of 500 pounds. Photo by Walter Deas at Wistari Reef.

315. *Epinephelus merra* Bloch. Honeycomb rock cod. The honeycomb pattern is quite distinctive in this individual. Photo by Allan Power.

316. *Epinephelus merra* Bloch. Again a species with many names, including honeycomb rock cod, spotted grouper, wire-netting cod, and Matty McMahon. The last name is used in Gladstone. Photo by Allan Power.

317.
Cromileptes altivelis
(Valenciennes). Hump-
backed rock cod. This
species is common in
the northern part of the
Great Barrier Reef.
Photo by Walter Deas.

318. *Epinephelus megachir* (Richardson). Long-finned rock cod. This species, which grows to about 14 inches, is apparently not common in Queensland. Photo by Walter Deas at Heron Island.

319. *Epinephelus megachir* (Richardson). The honeycomb pattern is similar to that of *E. merra*, but if you look closely you can see several differences. Photo by Walter Deas at Heron Island (30 feet deep).

320. *Epinephelus megachir* (Richardson). This individual is resting on its very long pectoral fins. These fins help identify this species. Photo by Walter Deas at Heron Island (20 feet deep).

321. *Cephalopholis pachycentron* (Cuvier and Valenciennes). Spotted-faced rock cod. A small variable grouper common on the northern part of the Great Barrier Reef. The spots referred to in the common name may not be present as in this photo. Photo by Walter Deas at Heron Island (40 feet deep).

322. *Anyperodon leucogrammicus* (Cuvier and Valenciennes). White-lined rock cod. An easily recognizable species although the characteristic white lines along the side are grayish here. Photo by Allan Power.

323. *Epinephelus kohleri* Schultz. This grouper has been turning up in many areas. It is surprising it remained undescribed for so long a time, but apparently it was confused with varieties of *E. flavocoeruleus*. Photo by Walter Deas at Heron Island (60 feet deep).

324. *Epinephelus fuscoguttatus* (Forsskal). Black rock cod. A spotted or blotchy pattern is common to many groupers. It aids in their camouflage among the weed covered rocks which they frequent. Photo by Allan Power.

325. *Epinephelus fasciatus* (Forsskal). Black-tipped rock cod. One of the more common and colorful groupers of the Queensland coast. Photo by Allan Power.

326. *Cephalopholis miniatus* (Forsskal).
What appears to be a rock ledge is
the underside of some plate coral.
Photo by Allan Power at Wistari
Reef (40 feet deep).

327. *Epinephelus tauvina* (Forsskal) being cleaned by two *Labroides dimidiatus*. The blue fish at the top are upside-down *Assessor macneilli* Whitley. A young *Bodianus axillaris* is behind the grouper's head. Photo by Walter Deas.

328. *Assessor macneilli* Whitley. A common fish on the Queensland coast most often seen swimming upside-down as in the above photo. Photo of a 3-inch male from Lizard Island by Dr. Gerald R. Allen (4 meters deep).

329. *Anthias squamipinnis* (Peters). Orange sea perch. A male with his elongate dorsal fin spine raised. Photo by Dr. Gerald R. Allen at Opal Reef in only five feet of water.

330. *Anthias squamipinnis* (Peters). These fishes have also been referred to as lyretail cods. Photo by Walter Deas.

331. *Anthias squamipinnis* (Peters). Orange sea perch are common in Queensland in deeper water. Photo by Allan Power.

332.
Anthias squamipinnis
(Peters). The golden
color of these females
blends well with the
similar color of the
Dendrophyllia polyps.
These fishes are also
apt to swim upside
down in caves. Photo
by Allan Power at Heron
Island (90 feet deep).

333. *Anthias squamipinnis* (Peters). Many fishes are often found around the corals. The *Anthias* are passing over it while the small yellow damselfishes are hovering close to it. Photo by Allan Power.

334. *Pseudochromis paccagnellae* Axelrod. One of the deep water species of the Great Barrier Reef. Photographed by Allan Power at 110 feet deep off Wistari Reef.

335. *Pseudochromis paccagnellae* Axelrod. The bright colors of this fish make it stand out from the rather drab background. The small fish is a goby. Photo by Walter Deas at Heron Island (55 feet deep).

336. A small group of snappers, *Lutjanus kasmira* (Forsskal), with a pair of Moorish idols, *Zanclus canescens* Linnaeus. The fishes in the background are damsels. Photo by Allan Power.

337. *Lutjanus johni* (Bloch). Spotted-scale sea perch. Note that the large dark spot on the side is mostly above the lateral line. Photo by Allan Power.

338. *Lutjanus bohar* (Forsskal). Red mumea. This snapper is one of the more poisonous species when eaten. A juvenile is shown here. Photo by Dr. Gerald R. Allen (20 feet deep).

339. *Lutjanus johni* (Bloch). This individual may have been attacked earlier as there is a section of the dorsal fin missing and a scar just below it. Photo by Walter Deas at Heron Island (40 feet deep).

340. *Lutjanus amabilis* (De Vis). Yellow-banded hussar. In proper lighting this fish is a pinkish color with a bright yellow lateral stripe. Photo by Allan Power.

341. *Lutjanus carponotatus* (Richardson). Stripey sea perch. A somewhat rare fish in Australia but found in the northern sector of the Great Barrier Reef. Photo by Walter Deas at Sykes Reef (45 feet deep).

343.
?*Lutjanus argenti-maculatus* (Forsskal). This was identified as the mangrove jack, but that species is supposed to have the anterior part of the soft anal fin and the pelvics dark. Photo by Allan Power.

342. *Lutjanus quinquelineatus* (Bloch). A school of small snappers seeking shelter among the branches of *Acropora* coral. Photo by Allan Power at Wistari Reef (50 feet deep).

344. *Lutjanus sebae* (Cuvier and Valenciennes). Red emperor. A snapper with many common names such as king snapper, government bream, queenfish, and Seba's snapper. It is considered a good sports fish as well as a sought after aquarium fish. Photo by Allan Power at North-West Island.

345.
Spilotichthys pictus
(Thunberg) and *Lutjanus sebae* (Cuvier). Different species will often school together temporarily. Here a red emperor gets mixed up with a school of sweetlips. Photo by Walter Deas.

346. *Symphorus nematophorus* (Bleeker). Chinaman-fish. This easily recognized snapper may be poisonous at times if eaten and is therefore avoided as a food fish. Photo by Roger Steene.

347. *Caesio erythrogaster* Cuvier and Valenciennes. Red-bellied fusilier. A common fish of the Great Barrier Reef, especially in the northern sector. It grows to over a foot in length. Photo by Roger Steene.

348. *Pterocaesio diagramma* (Bleeker). Dark banded fusilier. Two or three members of a school of fusiliers have stopped to be serviced by a cleaner wrasse, *Labroides*. Photo by Allan Power.

349. *Pterocaesio diagramma* (Bleeker). Schools of fusiliers are commonly seen in reef-type habitats. Photo by Walter Deas at Heron Island (50 feet deep).

350.
Spilotichthys pictus
(Thunberg). The painted
sweetlips grows to a
length of about two feet.
Photo by Walter Deas.

351. *Spilotichthys pictus* (Thunberg). Painted sweetlips. A school of adult sweetlips. The juveniles are very different from these in color pattern. Photo by Allan Power.

352. *Spilotichthys pictus* (Thunberg). The sweetlips remains nearly motionless as the two *Labroides* check it over. Photo by Allan Power.

353. *Spilotichthys pictus* (Thunberg). The sweetlips is checked inside and out. The *Labroides* can enter the mouth without fear of being eaten. Photo by Allan Power.

354.
Spilotichthys pictus
(Thunberg). Even these
larger fishes must seek
the protection of the
Acropora branches.
Perhaps it was the
photographer that
frightened them. Photo
by Allan Power at
Fitzroy Lagoon,
Capricorn Group
(30 feet).

355. *Gaterin punctatissimus* (Playfair). Multi-spotted sweetlips. A widespread species but not common on the Great Barrier Reef. It has only been recorded from north Queensland. Photo by Walter Deas at Heron Island (30 feet deep).

356. *Gaterin goldmanni* (Bleeker). Many-lined sweetlips. This two-foot-long fish is found only in the northern sections of Australia. Photo by Allan Power.

357. *Gaterin orientalis* (Bloch). Unlike the snappers and lethrinids, there are no canines in the jaws of the sweetlips. Photo by Allan Power.

358. *Gaterin punctatissimus* (Playfair). According to J.L.B. Smith, this may be the adult of *G. picus*. This fish seems to have remnants of the *picus* pattern. Photo by Walter Deas at Heron Island (30 feet deep).

359. *Gaterin punctatissimus* (Playfair). The adult of this species is very close to *G. chaetodonoides* and the two are hard to distinguish. The height of the soft dorsal fin is the clue. Photo by Walter Deas.

360. *Spilotichthys pictus* (Thunberg). In contrast to the silvery individuals shown earlier, this one has an orange-spotted pattern. Note also the dark lower lobe of the caudal fin. Photo by Allan Power.

Family LETHRINIDAE
EMPEROR BREAM

The emperor bream are well represented on the Great Barrier Reef with about a dozen species in our area of coverage. Some grow to a fairly good size, with the sweetlip emperor, *Lethrinus chrysostomus*, attaining a size of about three feet and a weight of 20 pounds. It is also the commonest species of emperor bream on the Queensland coast and is frequently sought after by fishermen. The sweetlip emperor is generally caught in the reef area as the fishing boat drifts over the inter-reef patches.

The anterior teeth of the emperor bream are cardiform, small and pointed with some enlarged canines. There is a single series of teeth laterally which are conical and pointed in young fishes. In some species the posterior lateral teeth develop into molar-like teeth, becoming rounded and flat. The emperors feed on fishes, crustaceans, and molluscs, hard shells and carapaces being crushed by the molars.

The distinguishing characters used to identify the different species are the type of teeth in the jaws (molar or non-molar laterally), the extent of the maxillary in relation to the eye, the number of scale rows between the dorsal fin base and the lateral line, some proportional measurements, and color pattern (even though they are variable fishes).

In Australia the emperors are good sports fish, not only putting up a good fight when hooked, but also being valued as food fish. They can be caught on the reef by hook and line like many snappers and grunts which congregate around the protection of the corals.

One of the emperors that is a valuable food fish around the Queensland area is the spangled emperor, *Lethrinus nebulosus*. This is an attractive species that reaches a length of about 2½ feet and is reportedly the second largest emperor on the Great Barrier Reef.

361. *Lethrinus chrysostomus* Richardson. Sweetlip emperor. This boldly marked *Lethrinus* is one of the commonest of the genus on the Great Barrier Reef. Photo by Allan Power.

362. *Lethrinus nebulosus* (Forsskal). Spangled emperor. A common food fish on the northern Queensland coasts which may also be called the morwong, sand snapper, green snapper, sand bream, or yellow sweetlip. Photo by Walter Deas on Wistari Reef (60 feet deep).

363. *Lethrinus chrysostomus* Richardson. A lateral view showing the scarlet markings characteristic of this species. Photo by Walter Deas at Heron Island (30 feet deep).

364.
Lethrinus chrysostomus
Richardson. Lethrinids
have the ability to
change color, as a
comparison of this
photo with those on the
previous pages will
show. Photo by Walter
Deas.

365. *Lethrinus* sp. Silvery fishes in open water are sometimes difficult to see. Photo by Walter Deas at Kenn Reef, outer Great Barrier Reef.

366. *Gymnocranius audleyi* Ogilby. Collared sea bream. A common fish that is utilized for food. Photo by Allan Power.

367. *Lethrinus* sp. A head-on view of the same species as that on the opposite page. The fins are probably red or pinkish. Photo by Allan Power.

368. *Scolopsis bilineatus* (Bloch). Yellow-finned spinecheek. A wide ranging fish also occurring on the Great Barrier Reef. Photo by Dr. Gerald R. Allen at Spur Reef of a 6-inch individual (30 feet deep).

369. *Scolopsis temporalis* (Cuvier). Barred-face spinecheek. This fish frequents areas of coral rubble and sand. Its diet consists of molluscs or crustaceans. Photo by Walter Deas at Heron Island (60 feet deep).

370. *Scolopsis margaritifer* (Cuvier). Pearly spinecheek. The upper lobe of the caudal fin is yellow and the lower lobe is said to be maroon at times. This one has obviously paled. Photo by Allan Power.

371. *Pentapodus setosus* (Cuvier and Valenciennes). Blue banded whiptail. The adult color pattern is just forming in this individual. The juvenile dark lateral band is starting to disappear. Photo by Roger Steene.

372. *Gnathodentex aurolineatus* (Lacepede). Gold-lined sea bream. Perhaps the common name should be gold spot or white spot, for this character is outstanding in this fish. Photo by Allan Power.

Family THERAPONIDAE
TIGERFISHES

The tigerfishes comprise a small family of fishes with only three genera recognized. These three genera, *Therapon, Pelates*, and *Helotes*, are distinguishable by the type and number of teeth in the jaws. *Helotes* has flattened tricuspid teeth as distinguished from the other two genera in which the teeth are simple. *Therapon* has the teeth in a viliform band whereas *Pelates* has only two (lower jaw) to three (upper jaw) series.

The body is ovate, compressed, covered with small to moderate scales. The dorsal fin is notched and provided with 12-13 spines. The anal has the usual three spines and about 7-12 rays.

In Australia, although they grow to a size of about 5 pounds, the marine forms are not as valued for food as are the fresh water forms.

About five species of *Therapon* are found in Queensland waters, one of which, *Therapon jarbua*, the crescent perch, is very well known. They are distinguishable by the spination of the opercle and preopercle, by color pattern, and by scale counts.

The trumpeter perch, *Pelates quadrilineatus*, is commonly encountered on the sand flats of Moreton Bay. It attains a length of about 8 inches and is marked with a number of dark brown horizontal stripes (although the juveniles have 8-9 broad dark bars as well).

Helotes sexlineatus, the six-lined perch, is also horizontally striped, although the juveniles have several dark blotches on the back. This species grows slightly larger than the previous one, reaching up to 11 inches in length.

373. *Therapon jarbua* (Forsskal). Crescent perch. This fish can easily travel into pure fresh water. It is distinguishable by the curved stripes on the body. Photo by Roger Steene.

Family CEPOLIDAE
BAND-FISHES

The remarkable similarity of the species of band-fishes can be seen by comparing the photo of *Cepola australis* presented here and that of *Acanthocepola indica* from PMF-4, pp. 930-931. The other species of band-fishes are also very similar and identification is often fairly difficult. Characters such as the presence or absence of a dark spot in the dorsal fin, the dorsal and anal fin ray counts, and body proportions help distinguish the species, as does the presence of certain dark marks on or about the maxillary bones, although this last character is generally too vague or variable to be of much use for specific identification.

The color of the band-fishes is generally some shade of red or pink, often with orange markings on the side in the form of spots or stripes. The orange vertical stripes are not prominent in the photo below, but they are visible.

Unlike the Japanese who utilize the band-fishes for food, the Australians consider them of little use, the flesh being rather dry and there being too many bones.

A single species of band-fish, *Cepola australis*, has been recorded from our area of coverage, it being found in the southern part of Queensland. It is more of a southern Australian species with a range extending from South Australia around New South Wales to southern Queensland. It is known simply as band-fish and grows to a length of about 10 to 15 inches. The specimen illustrated is probably rather small, but since there are no reports of drastic changes occurring from juvenile to adult in this family of fishes, it should represent the species quite well. The dorsal fin is said to have about 55-60 rays, the anal fin 48-55. The mouth is provided with small, pointed teeth.

374. *Cepola australis* Ogilby. Band-fish. This band-fish is restricted to Australia although it has very close relatives in the China Sea. Photo by Roger Steene.

Family MONOCENTRIDAE
PINECONE FISHES

The pinecone fishes, or knight-fishes as they are called in Australia, are small fishes (no more than about 9 inches) that have the body entirely encased in a hard bony armor composed of thick bony scales which bear sharp spines. Fishes so constricted by armor are generally thought to be poor swimmers, and the knight-fishes are no exception. They can easily be captured in hand nets and it is often possible to trap them by hand.

They possess light organs, which are commonly considered a feature of deep water fishes. The pinecone fishes, at least the Australian species *Monocentris gloriamaris*, sometimes can be found in shallow water, the light organs being used primarily at night. These small fishes move slowly above the bottom, the light organs (which are directed downwards) aiding the fish in detecting the small shrimps that form part of its diet.

Pinecone fishes are avidly sought after as aquarium fishes and usually command very high prices. Although easily captured, they are difficult to find—during the day they are secretive and hide in caves or under ledges where they are not so easily detected, and at night the decreased visibility makes them more difficult to locate. When caught in relatively deeper water the fish must be decompressed, as a quick journey to the surface will have serious consequences. Usually the knight-fish will be seen in small groups or at least in pairs, rarely if ever alone.

This species has an unusual distribution, occurring from Queensland to Western Australia and also dubiously recorded from South Africa. Prawn trawlers in southern Queensland have caught a number of these fishes and it may not be as rare as previously suspected.

In New South Wales the knight-fish is referred to as the port-and-starboard-light fish, in reference, of course, to the light organs. Live specimens when placed in aquaria will, in the evening hours or in dim light, be seen with the lights shining.

The Australian knight-fish grows to about 9 inches. The individual pictured here is a young fish.

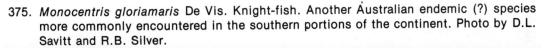

375. *Monocentris gloriamaris* De Vis. Knight-fish. Another Australian endemic (?) species more commonly encountered in the southern portions of the continent. Photo by D.L. Savitt and R.B. Silver.

376.
Upeneichthys porosus
(Cuvier and
Valenciennes). Blue-
spotted goatfish.
Several individuals in
the day pattern and one
(reddish fish) in the
night color. Photo by
Walter Deas.

377. *Upeneichthys porosus* (Cuvier and Valenciennes). The night color of the blue-spotted goatfish. Notice the barbel sticking out in front. Photo by Walter Deas.

378.
Petroscirtes sp. This is probably a Batesian mimic of *Meiacanthus lineatus* (De Vis). The food of both these species is invertebrates. Photo by Dr. Gerald R. Allen at Lizard Island (10 feet deep).

379.
Plagiotremus tapeinosoma (Bleeker). Violet-banded blenny. Any hole in the reef may become a home for this blenny. This fish is not stuck but can move in and out of its entrance with ease. Photo by Dr. Gerald R. Allen of a 4-inch individual from One Tree Island.

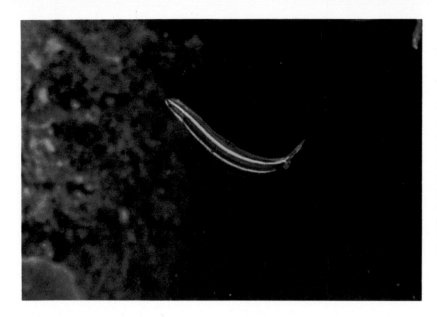

380.
*Plagiotremus
rhynorhynchos*
(Bleeker). Cleaner
mimic. An unusual
photo of this species in
open water. Most often
when a photographer
approaches it retreats
into its burrow. Photo
by Walter Deas.

381. *Plagiotremus rhynorhynchos* (Bleeker). A more usual pose half in and half out of its burrow. These fishes may actually bite swimmers, but the effects are not serious. Photo by Allan Power.

382. *Meiacanthus atrodorsalis atrodorsalis* (Gunther). This subspecies is widely distributed in the tropical Pacific. It is interesting to note that it is replaced in the Fiji Islands by the yellow subspecies *M.a. oualanensis*. Photo by Allan Power.

383. *Plagiotremus tapeinosoma* (Bleeker). Characteristic of this genus is a pair of well-developed anterior canines. Photo by Dr. Gerald R. Allen at One Tree Island (5 feet deep).

384.
Atrosalarias sp.
Blennies can be brightly
colored like this one
and would make very
fine aquarium
inhabitants. Photo by
Dr. Gerald R. Allen of a
2-inch individual from
Lizard Island (15 feet
deep).

385.
Eleotriodes longipinnis
(Bennett). Ocellated
gudgeon. A wide spread
species which occurs
from southern Japan to
Australia (Queensland)
and across the Pacific to
Samoa. Photo by
Aaron Norman.

386.
*Amblygobius
decussatus* (Bleeker).
The bright orange lines
usually stand out much
plainer than in this
photo. The fish is
against a light
background and may
have faded. Photo by Dr.
Gerald R. Allen at Lizard
Island (16 feet deep).

387.
Cryptocentrus koumansi
(Whitley). This goby
(which may also go
under the name
*Acentrogobius
koumansi*) sits side by
side with an alphaeid
shrimp which helps
construct the burrow.
Photo by Dr. Gerald R.
Allen of a 2-inch fish at
Lizard Island (7 feet
deep).

388. Different species of goby share lodgings with burrowing shrimps. Here a species of goby (1½ inches long) stands guard as the shrimp comes out of the burrow. Photo by Dr. Gerald R. Allen at One Tree Island (4 feet deep).

389. *Amblygobius rainfordi*. A brightly patterned species which rarely is imported for the marine fish enthusiast. Smith places this species in genus *Seychellia*. Photo by Dr. Gerald R. Allen at One Tree Island (10 feet deep).

390. *Ctenogobius maculosus* (Fourmanoir). Gobies are commonly found among the coral rubble of reef areas. They will sit like this propped up on their pelvic fins, ready to dart away if necessary. Photo by Dr. Gerald R. Allen of a 2-inch individual from One Tree Island.

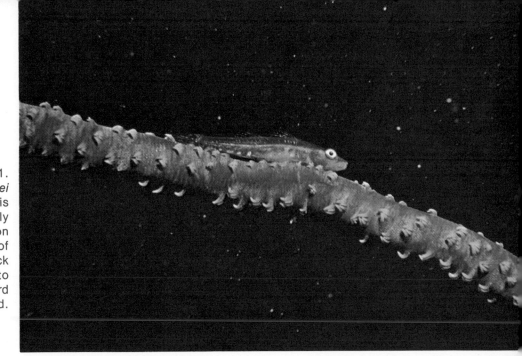

391.
Cottogobius yongei
Davis and Cohen. This
goby is normally
encountered on
branches of
antipatharian or black
coral sea whips. Photo
by Walter Deas at Lizard
Island.

392. *Cottogobius yongei* Davis and Cohen. The sucker-like pelvic fins help maintain the fish in position when water currents are strong. Photo by Dr. Gerald R. Allen at Euston Reef.

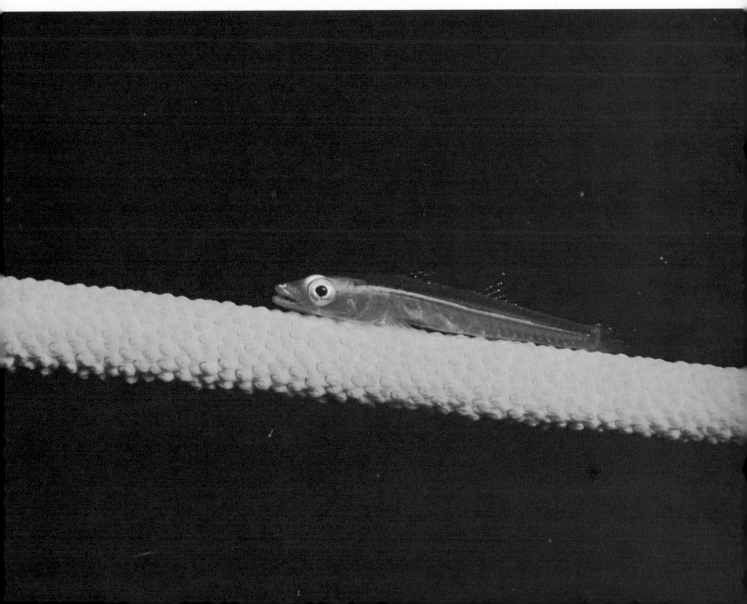

393. *Ostracion cubicus* Linnaeus. A small yellow cube with black spots and fins is a pretty fair description of the juvenile of this species. Photo by Walter Deas at Heron Island (20 feet deep).

Family OSTRACIONTIDAE
TRUNKFISHES

The trunkfishes are small to moderate sized fishes in which the body is encased in a carapace that might be triangular, square, or even pentagonal in cross section. The plates of this armor are modified scales which themselves are pentagonal or hexagonal in shape. The exposed parts of the body, few in number, are covered with smooth skin. The dorsal and anal fins are small, about equal in size, and placed opposite one another. These fins have no spines, the spinous portions along with the ventral fins having been lost.

Trunkfishes are quite easy to catch by net and can often be caught by hand like the knight-fishes. They are shy fishes normally found hiding among the corals or under ledges. The mouth is small and the jaws are provided with a row of long narrow teeth. One method in which these fishes hunt prey is to move over a sandy area blowing jets of water into the sand. This action often exposes small crustaceans or other invertebrates that have sought refuge in the sand.

Many of the trunkfishes are very colorful with variously colored spots or reticulated lines. The females are often differently colored than the males but just as brightly patterned.

Much of the taxonomy of the trunkfishes is based on the carapace. For instance, the robust boxfish, *Strophiurichthys robustus* (a member of the Great Barrier Reef fauna), has a carapace which ends before the dorsal and anal fin bases are covered. This is characteristic of several Australian genera, including *Aracana*. Other genera (with the carapace enclosing at least the anal fin) are distinguishable by the number and placement of the ridges and spines. *Lactoria,* for instance, has preocular spines and in addition has spines on the lower posterior corners of the carapace. The lateral ridges of *Lactophrys* are absent or nearly so, whereas those of the other Queensland genera are prominent. *Ostracion* has no dorsal ridge, a convex back, and rounded lateral and pelvic ridges in contrast to *Rhyncostracion* which has a low dorsal ridge, a flattened back, and sharp lateral and pelvic ridges.

394. *Ostracion cubicus* Linnaeus. An adult of the juvenile on the opposite page. Note the white spots bordered by black spots on the carapace. Photo by Allan Power.

395. *Arothron stellatus* (Bloch and Schneider). Starry toado. A widespread Indo-Pacific species known in Australia from the east, north and west coasts, mostly in warm water. Photo by Walter Deas.

396. *Sphoeroides hamiltoni* (Gray and Richardson). Common toado. A very common fish in inshore areas where they can be easily captured. Photo by Roger Steene.

397.
Arothron stellatus
(Bloch and Schneider).
A young form of the
adult shown on the
opposite page. These
fishes may be
poisonous when eaten.
Photo by Allan Power.

398. *Arothron immaculatus* (Bloch and Schneider). Plain toado or narrow-lined toadfish. The lined pattern is distinctive but may not always be present. Grows to about a foot in length. Photo by Klaus Paysan.

399.
Canthigaster valentini
(Bleeker). Black-saddled
puffer. This species has
been placed in
Tetraodon and
Psilonotus at one time
or another, but
Canthigaster is almost
universally accepted
nowadays. Photo by
Walter Deas.

400. *Canthigaster valentini* (Bleeker). It is difficult to photograph a sharp-nosed puffer with its tail expanded. Photo by Walter Deas at Heron Island (25 feet deep).

Family TETRAODONTIDAE
PUFFERS

The puffers are not encased in a bony carapace like the boxfishes, but they are slow-moving fishes nevertheless. They are well-known for their ability to inflate themselves with water (or air if they are removed from the water) as a defensive mechanism. This has earned them the common names of puffers, blowfish, or swellfish. The Australians refer to them as toados.

There are three genera reported from Queensland waters, *Sphoeroides, Arothron*, and *Chelonodon*. These are basically distinguishable by the structure of the nostrils. *Sphoeroides* has the nostrils with two distinct openings usually at the tip of a nasal tube or papillae. *Arothron* on the other hand has the nostrils on each side with a bifid tentacle lacking a distinct opening. The third genus, *Chelonodon*, has a nostril with a raised tube which has two marginal flaps or a fringe. These genera are represented in Queensland waters by about 18 species. *Chelonodon*, a genus with few species, includes one from the Great Barrier Reef, the marbled toado, *C. patoca*. *Arothron* includes many species of which about eight occur in Queensland waters, none endemic. The third genus, *Sphoeroides*, also includes many species of which about nine are found in our area of coverage. Five of these (*Sphoeroides pleurogramma, S. pleurostictus, S. tuberculiferus, S. whitleyi*, and *S. squamicauda*) are only from Australian waters and one of these five is restricted to Queensland.

Most puffers (excluding of course the sharp-nosed puffers of the genus *Canthigaster*) are too large for aquaria when fully grown. Those from Australia range in size from about 6 inches up to two feet in length, with the exception of the endemic scaly-tailed toado, *Sphoeroides squamicauda*, which may reach its maximum size at about 4 inches or so.

401. *Arothron nigropunctatus* (Bloch and Schneider). Black-spotted toado. A wide ranging species but not common in Queensland or New South Wales. Considered poisonous if eaten. Photo by Dr. Gerald R. Allen (30 feet deep).

402.
Dicotylichthys myersi
Ogilby. Myer's
porcupine fish. Very
similar to species of
Diodon but separated
from that genus on·the
basis of having
confluent nostrils.
Photo by Walter Deas.

403. *Oxymonacanthus longirostris* (Bloch and Schneider). Beaked leatherjacket. One of the aquarium favorites in the plectognaths, it is at home among the branching corals like *Acropora*. Photo by Dr. Gerald R. Allen (30 feet deep).

Family MONACANTHIDAE
FILEFISHES

Approximately five genera of filefishes or leatherjackets occur in the waters of the Great Barrier Reef. *Alutera* and *Osbeckia* are sometimes separated as a family, but we feel they should be included in the Monacanthidae. They differ from each other by the caudal fin length (shorter than head in *Alutera*, longer in *Osbeckia*) and shape of the snout. Both these genera differ from the other filefishes in having lost the pelvic fins (these are fused into a spiny process in the remaining genera). Of the four remaining genera, *Oxymonacanthus* is easily distinguishable by its elongate snout. *Cantherhines* is recognizable by its immovable pelvic spine (a character which aquarists may have difficulty in ascertaining unless the fish in question can be handled), and *Chaetoderma* has large dermal filaments on the body and dorsal spine which are lacking in *Monacanthus*.

Monacanthus filicauda, the thread-tailed leatherjacket, occurs from New Guinea to Queensland in relatively deep water (between 100 and 200 feet) although it may be encountered in shallower water occasionally.

Probably one of the more unusual of the filefishes is the prickly leatherjacket, *Chaetoderma pencilligera*. In this species the dermal filaments are greatly developed, looking very much like some alga is covering the body and giving the fish a means of concealment among real algae. This fish is relatively common on the Queensland coast.

Unlike the triggerfishes, which are closely related to the filefishes, the filefishes have a small nipping mouth with which they eat small invertebrates and algae. Triggerfishes have larger mouths with a strong set of teeth with which they can break off or nibble on pieces of coral, crustaceans, sea urchins, and the like. In other words, if you have filefishes and triggerfishes in your aquarium, be a lot more wary of being bitten by the trigger than by the filefish.

404. *Monacanthus filicauda* (Gunther). Thread-tailed leatherjacket. This photo can now be compared with the illustration on p. 1355 (Book 5). It is apparently a deep water fish, being trawled in depths of 19 to 28 fathoms. Photo by Roger Steene.

405. *Alutera scripta* (Forster). Figured leatherjacket. Night color. This species occasionally is seen in Queensland usually north of Townsville. Photo by Allan Power.

406.
Cantherhines howensis
(Ogilby). Many of the
filefishes in Australia
are quite different from
those in other parts of
the world. This brightly
colored species is
assuming a defensive
posture with its dorsal
spine raised. Photo by
Walter Deas.

407. *Cantherhines howensis* (Ogilby). The name *howensis* refers to Lord Howe Island, although this species occurs in Queensland as well. Photo by Walter Deas at Wistari Reef (40 feet deep).

408. *Balistoides niger* (Bonnaterre). This is one of the youngest clown triggerfish ever photographed. Note the differences in color pattern between it and the adults on this and the page opposite. Photo by Dr. Herbert R. Axelrod.

409. *Balistoides niger* (Bonnaterre). There is no problem spotting a clown triggerfish on the reef. The white dorsal spots of the juvenile have disappeared. Photo by Dr. Gerald R. Allen of a 10-inch individual at Euston Reef (30 feet deep).

410. *Balistoides niger* (Bonnaterre). With a color pattern like this and the ease with which it is kept in captivity, no wonder this fish commands a high price. Photo by Walter Deas.

411. *Antennarius striatus* (Shaw and Nodder). Striped angler. A fairly common anglerfish that reaches Australia. It is said to be more common in the southern sector of the Great Barrier Reef than in the northern part. Photo by Walter Deas.

412. *Antennarius phymatodes* Bleeker. A strikingly patterned angler that occasionally appears for sale. The pattern is very similar to that of the fish illustrated on p. 530 (Book 2) from the Philippines. Photo by Dr. Herbert R. Axelrod.

Index

Page numbers in **bold** face refer to illustrations

The following index contains entries for subject matter and illustrations contained in this book and its companion volumes, *Pacific Marine Fishes*, 1-6. Some of the names used in earlier volumes of this series, however, have been revised to reflect an updated or otherwise changed nomenclatural standing; all such names listed in text and index of these volumes are listed in this index but are referenced to show the revised identifications.

A

Abalistes stellaris, **395**, **1344**
Ablennes anastomella, 332
Ablennes hians, **924**, **926**
Abudefduf, 701
Abudefduf affinis, 1025
Abudefduf amabilis, 304
Abudefduf annulatus, 738
Abudefduf aureus, **305**, **1564**
Abudefduf aureus, **196**
  (See *Chromis analis*)
Abudefduf behni, **200**, **206**, **1036**, **1564**
Abudefduf bengalensis, **194**, **1715**
Abudefduf biocellatus, **204**, **732**, **733**, **1714**
Abudefduf bitaeniatus, **206**
  (See *Abudefduf behni*)
Abudefduf curacao, **1023**
Abudefduf cyaneus, **190**, **192**, **193**, **197**, **203**, **302**, **1036**
Abudefduf dickii, **730**, **1028**, **1559**
Abudefduf dickii, **201**
  (See *Abudefduf johnstonianus*)
Abudefduf flavipinnis, **1037**, **1713**
Abudefduf glaucus, **734**, **1033**, **1716**
Abudefduf johnstonianus, **201**
Abudefduf lacrymatus, **207**, **731**, **735**, **1029**
Abudefduf leucogaster, **200**, **304**, **1558**
Abudefduf leucopomus, **1032**, **1035**, **1714**
Abudefduf leucozona, **307**, **1034**, **1035**
Abudefduf melanopus, **203**, **306**, **307**, **1034**
Abudefduf oxyodon, **206**
Abudefduf palmeri, **1715**
Abudefduf parasema, 303
Abudefduf parasema, **203**
  (See *Abudefduf cyaneus*)
Abudefduf phoenixensis, **307**
Abudefduf rex, **202**, **1031**
Abudefduf rollandi, **1715**
Abudefduf saxatilis, **195**, **1023**, **1024**, **1025**, **1617**
Abudefduf septemfasciatus, **1023**
Abudefduf sexfasciatus, **195**, **736**, **1024**

Abudefduf sordidus, **194**, **306**, **727**, **728**, **729**
Abudefduf sparoides, **737**
Abudefduf thoracotaeniatus, **195**
Abudefduf unimaculatus, **1714**
Abudefduf uniocellata, **190**, **192**, **197**
  (See *Abudefduf cyaneus*)
Abudefduf vaigiensis, **737**
Abudefduf whitleyi, **1561**, **1661**, **1715**
Abudefduf xanthonotus, **203**
  (See *Abudefduf melanopus*)
Abudefduf xanthurus, **200**
  (See *Abudefduf behni*)
Abudefduf sp., **201**
  (See *Pomacentrus dorsalis*)
Abudefduf sp., **200**
  (See *Abudefduf leucogaster*)
Acanthocepola, 931
Acanthocepola indica, **930**, **931**, **1888**
Acanthochromis polyacanthus, **1558**, **1726**
Acanthogobius flavimanus, 179
Acanthopagrus berda, 1314
ACANTHURIDAE, 84, 793, 1607
Acanthurus, 803
Acanthurus bariene, 1610
Acanthurus bleekeri, **384**, **1748**
Acanthurus chronixis, **796**, **1607**, **1609**
Acanthurus dussumieri, **385**, **1617**, **1744**
Acanthurus gahhm, **382**, **796**, **1612**
Acanthurus glaucopareius, 91, **386**, **1747**
Acanthurus guttatus, 384
Acanthurus japonicus, 91, **386**
Acanthurus leucosternon, 85, **381**, **797**
Acanthurus lineatus, 85, 90, **387**, **1148**, **1149**, **1607**, **1610**, **1611**, **1747**
Acanthurus mata, **1610**, **1745**
Acanthurus nigrofuscus, 86
Acanthurus olivaceous, 86, **383**, **1746**
Acanthurus pyroferus, 89, **1607**, **1608**, **1609**
Acanthurus tennenti, 795
Acanthurus triostegus, 90, **792**, **793**

Acanthurus xanthopterus, **1612**
Acanthurus sp., 794
Acentrogobius cauerensis, 635
Acentrogobius hoshinonis, 178
Acentrogobius koumansi, 1895
Acentrogobius ornatus, **1014**
Acentrogobius sp., **1014**
Achoerodus gouldii, 1732
Adenapogon, 1681
Adioryx, 230, 231, 689
Adioryx andamanensis, 691
Adioryx caudimaculatus, **339**, **691**, **1451**, **1458**
Adioryx cornutum, **1457**, **1689**
Adioryx diadema, **234**, **1061**, **1452**
Adioryx lacteoguttatus, **339**, **693**, **1063**
Adioryx microstomus, 339
Adioryx rubra, **235**, **1062**, **1690**
Adioryx spinifer, **234**, **689**, **690**, **692**, **1454**, **1456**, **1691**, **1692**, **1693**
Adioryx spinosissimus, **1061**
Adioryx tiere, 341
Adioryx tieroides, **1458**
Adioryx violaceus, **1454**, **1455**
Adioryx xantherythrus, 230, 340
Adioryx sp., **1061**
Aeoliscus, 319
Aeoliscus strigatus, **320**, **321**, **1416**, **1417**
Aesopia, 1099
Aesopia heterorhinos, 1099
Aetobatus, 1672
Aetobatus narinari, **1076**, **1671**, **1672**
Aetomylaeus, 1077
African clown wrasse, **578**
African squirrelfish, 235
Aholeholes, **236**, 308
Albula vulpes, **1043**
Alectis ciliaris, **1050**
Alectis indica, 426, **1050**
Alectis major, **1051**
ALEPISAURIDAE, 1257
Alepisaurus borealis, **1256**
Alepisaurus ferox, **1257**
Alfoncino, 548, 1161
Allard's clownfish, 705
Alutera, 1905
Alutera monoceros, **125**

Alutera scripta, **122, 1356, 1632, 1633, 1906**
ALUTERIDAE, 819
Amanses scopas, **1350, 1351, 1631**
AMARSIPIDAE, 1220
Amblyapistus taenianotus, **517, 962, 1624**
Amblycirrhitus, 155, 660
Amblycirrhitus bimacula, **1142**
Amblygobius albimaculatus, **634, 635**
Amblygobius decussatus, **1600, 1894**
Amblygobius phalaena, **1602**
Amblygobius rainfordi, **1896**
Amora, 219
Amphiprion, 181, 287
Amphiprion akindynos, **288, 292, 1698, 1699, 1700-1702, 1704**
Amphiprion allardi, 701, **705, 708**
Amphiprion biaculeatus, **190, 301**
   (= *Premnas biaculeatus*)
Amphiprion chrysopterus, **191, 296, 297, 1019, 1547, 1551**
Amphiprion clarkii, 180, **183, 185, 292, 704, 708, 709, 714, 715, 1018, 1019, 1547, 1548, 1551**
Amphiprion ephippium, 292
Amphiprion frenatus, 184, **186, 187, 1020, 1021**
Amphiprion latezonatus, 289
Amphiprion laticlavius, 183
Amphiprion melanopus, **293, 1545, 1551, 1552, 1696, 1697**
Amphiprion nigripes, **561, 710, 711, 712, 713, 714**
Amphiprion ocellaris, **188, 189, 298, 299, 300, 301, 1021**
Amphiprion percula, 188
Amphiprion perideraion, **182, 185, 294, 295, 1017, 1545, 1548, 1549, 1550, 1703, 1705**
Amphiprion polymnus, 183
Amphiprion sandaracinos, 188
Amphiprion tricinctus, **290, 291**
Amphiprion xanthurus, 180
Amphiprion sp., **706, 707**
Amphotistius kuhli, **1394, 1395**
Anago anago, 352
Anampses caeruleopunctatus, **144, 145, 440, 623**
Anampses cuvieri, 445
Anampses meleagrides, **442, 864**
Anampses neoguinaicus, 863
Anampses rubrocaudatus, 440
   (= *Anampses chrysocephalus*)
Anampses twistii, 440, **863**
Anampses sp., 142
   (See *Anampses neoguinaicus*)
Anemonefishes, 181, 289, 701, 1545
Angelfishes, 7, 39, 781
Angel sharks, 1069
Anglerfish, **509**
Anglerfishes, 258
Anguilla, 260
Anguilla japonica, **351**

ANOMALOPIDAE, 1411
Anomalops katoptron, **1411**
ANTENNARIIDAE, 258
Antennarius biocellatus, **828**
Antennarius chironectes, **529**
Antennarius coccineus, **529**
Antennarius hispidus, **528**
Antennarius indicus, **529**
Antennarius nox, 259
Antennarius nummifer, **258, 1365**
Antennarius phymatodes, **530, 1910**
Antennarius sanguifluus, 259
Antennarius striatus, **1910**
Antennarius tridens, **259, 270, 532**
Antennarius sp., **528**
Anthias, 643
Anthias hutchi, **1469, 1471**
Anthias pleurotaenia, **1467, 1468, 1470**
Anthias squammipinnis, **489, 490, 649, 1224, 1857, 1859, 1860, 1861**
Anthias sp., **646, 742, 760, 1467**
Anthiinae, 489, 643
Anyperodon, 643
Anyperodon leucogrammicus, **491, 647, 1851**
Aphareus, 675
Aphareus flavivultus, 675
Aphareus furcatus, 675
Aphareus rutilans, **1293**
Apistus carinatus, **533**
Apodes, 260
Apogon, 241, 678, 1681
Apogon apogonoides, **463**
Apogon aroubiensis, **1430, 1436, 1683**
Apogon aureus, **1447, 1678**
Apogon compressus, **1434, 1435**
Apogon cyanosoma, **243, 679, 967, 1434, 1435**
Apogon doderleini, **1682**
Apogon erythrinus, **463**
Apogon exostigma, **463**
Apogon fasciatus, **460**
Apogon fraenatus, **460, 1439**
Apogon fragilis, **1442, 1685**
Apogon fuscus, **461**
Apogon hartzfeldi, **1437, 1683**
Apogon kallopterus, **1438**
Apogon leptacanthus, **460, 1443, 1685**
Apogon lineatus, **968**
Apogon nematopterus, **243, 464, 465**
Apogon niger, **967**
Apogon novemfasciatus, **242, 969**
Apogon nubilis, **679, 686**
Apogon orbicularis, **243**
   (See *Apogon nematopterus*)
Apogon robustus, **242**
Apogon savayensis, **678, 1446**
Apogon sealei, **1439**
Apogon semilineatus, **240, 462**
Apogon snyderi, **686**
Apogon taeniophorus, **1436**
Apogon taeniopterus, **461**
Apogon thermalis, **1685**

Apogon trimaculatus, **968**
Apogon uninotatus, 241
Apogon sp., **1437, 1440, 1678, 1679, 1680, 1681**
Apogonichthyoides, 678
Apogonichthyoides taeniatus, 685
APOGONIDAE, **241, 678, 1432, 1681**
Apolemichthys, 786
Apolemichthys arcuatus, **364**
Apolemichthys trimaculatus, **364, 785, 1126, 1127, 1128, 1533**
Apolemichthys xanthurus, **784, 785**
Aprion virescens, **1293**
Aptychotrema, 1677
Arabian pike-eel, 351
Aracana, 1899
Aracana aurita, **1363**
Archamia, 678
Archamia biguttata, **1445**
Archamia fucata, 682, **686, 1444, 1445, 1446**
Archamia leai, **1441**
Archamia zosterophora, **1442**
Archamia sp., **1440**
Archerfishes, 327
Arctoscopus japonicus, **273**
Argus-wrasse, 455
Argyrops spinifer, **1312**
Argyrosomus argentatus, **1321**
Argyrosomus japonicus, **1320**
Argyrosomus nibea, **1320**
Armorheads, 1217
Arnoglossus, 262
Arothron, 97, 1903
Arothron aerostaticus, **104**
Arothron alboreticulatus, **105**
Arothron citrinellus, **112, 403**
Arothron hispidus, 106, **107, 109, 113, 409, 1634, 1636**
Arothron immaculatus, **1636, 1901**
Arothron mappa, **1637**
Arothron meleagris, **112**
Arothron nigropunctatus, **104, 403, 404, 1903**
Arothron niphobles, 113, **408**
Arothron pardalis, **108**
Arothron reticularis, **407**
Arothron rubripes, **406**
Arothron stellatus, 190, **1357, 1900, 1901**
Arothron stictonotus, **405**
Arothron vermicularis, **409**
Arothron sp., **404**
Aspasmichthys ciconae, 165, **1009**
Aspidontus taeniatus, 159, **471, 1333, 1595**
Assasi triggerfish, **125**
   (See black-bellied triggerfish)
Assessor macneilli, **1856**
Atrosalarias sp., **1894**
Astrapogon, 241
Astroconger myriaster, **275**
ATHERINIDAE, 1412
Aulacocephalus temmincki, 252, **495**
AULOPODIDAE, 913

Aulopus japonicus, 914
Aulopus purpurissatus, 914
AULOSTOMIDAE, 773, 1799, 1800
Aulostomus chinensis, 722, 773
  1423, 1799, 1800, 1801, 1802
Auxis thazard, 1328

B
Balistapus, 815
Balistapus undulatus, 119, 124, 646,
  818, 819, 1349, 1630
Balistes flavimarginatus, 1342, 1343
BALISTIDAE, 114, 815
Balistoides niger, 114, 115, 116, 123,
  396, 814, 815, 1111, 1340, 1341,
  1342, 1908, 1909
Balistoides viridescens, 393, 396,
  817
Band-fishes, 932, 1888
Banded catshark, 502
Banded cheilinus, 446, 569
Banded pipefish, 325
Banded-tailed goatfish, 344
Banded wrasse, 144, 582
Bar-chested damselfish, 195
Barhead spinefoot, 93, 94
Barracuda, 698
Barracudas, 925
Barred jack, 424
Barred morwong, 247, 481
Barred perch, 166
Barred squirrelfish, 234
Batfishes, 78, 525, 1138
Bathygobius fuscus, 174, 1014, 1015
BATRACHOIDIDAE, 1821
Beaked butterflyfish, 73
Bearded goby, 178
Beardfishes, 1173
Bellowsfish, 319, 322
BELONIDAE, 329
Bembras japonicus, 1007
Bengal devil, 194
Bennett's butterflyfish, 48, 64, 748
Bennett's sharpnosed puffer, 402
Berry frogfish, 529
BERYCIDAE, 1161
Beryx decadactylus, 549, 1161
Beryx splendens, 48, 1160, 1161
Bicolor cleaner wrasse, 136, 593
Bicolored parrotfish, 154, 458
Bigeye sea-bream, 435
Bigeye squirrelfish, 232
Bigeyes, 231, 551
Big-spine squirrelfish, 233
Big-teeth cardinalfish, 461
Bi-ocellated wrasse, 454
Bird wrasse, 129, 142, 143, 586, 852
Black-and-white snapper, 288
Black-and-white striped blenny, 164
Black-backed butterflyfish, 42, 377
Black-bar devil, 201
Black-bellied triggerfish, 125
Black-belt wrasse, 131, 443
Black-edge angelfish, 17
Blackfin gurnard, 536
Black-finned anemonefish, 714

Blackfinned triggerfish, 397
Black-finned triple-spine, 391
Blackfish, 546
Black porgy, 237, 438
Black ribbon eel, 275
Blackspot goatfish, 343
Blackspot tuskfish, 859
Black-spotted puffer, 104, 403
Black-tailed damselfish, 204
Blacktip soldierfish, 233, 340
Black-velvet angelfish, 362
Blanquillos, 531
Bleeker's surgeonfish, 384
Blennies, 159, 636, 1591
BLENNIIDAE, 159, 636, 1591
Blennius yatabei, 168
Blind goby, 478
Blotched filefish, 126
Blue-and-gold striped snapper, 227
Blue-and-yellow angelfish, 17
Blue-and-yellow rock cod, 494
Bluebacked puffer, 405
Blue chromis, 190
Blue-faced angelfish, 30, 31, 359,
  783
Blue-faced blenny, 169
Blue-finned triggerfish, 393
Bluefish, 1266
Blue-girdled angelfish, 28, 29, 360,
  361
Blue gudgeon, 477
Blue-line goby, 171
Blue-line pipefish, 325
Blue-lined angelfish, 32, 34, 35
Blue-lined grouper, 492
Blue-lined snapper, 227
Blue reef-fish, 190, 197
Blue ribbon eel, 275, 350
Blue-ringed angelfish, 26, 367
Blue-spotted goby, 178
Blue-spotted porgy, 437
Blue-spotted ray, 509
Blue-spotted snapper, 435
Blue-spotted wrasse, 144
Blue-streak devil, 206
Blue-streak weever, 473
Bluestripe butterflyfish, 374
Blue-striped snapper, 221
Blue tang, 87, 381
  Frontispiece (Book II), 1148
Blue-trim parrotfish, 154
Blue whiting, 135, 531
Blushing cardinalfish, 463
Blushing wrasse, 137
Boarfishes, 1217
Bodianus, 577, 587
Bodianus axillaris, 442, 577, 590,
  591, 854, 855, 1679, 1736, 1737
Bodianus bilunulatus, 143, 445, 856
Bodianus diana, 131, 587, 591, 854,
  858, 1579
Bodianus hirsutus, 856
Bodianus loxozonus, 1578, 1736
Bodianus luteopunctatus, 588, 589
Bodianus mesothorax, 131, 443, 854,
  858, 1578

Bodianus oxycephalus, 130, 133, 879
Bodianus perdito, 857, 858
Bodianus sp., 442, 444
Bolbometapon bicolor, 154, 458,
  984, 985, 1586
Boleophthalmus, 172
Bombay ducks, 913
BOTHIDAE, 262
Bothus, 262
Bothus sp., 1095
Boxfishes, 114
Brachirus biocellatus, 524, 945, 946,
  947
Brama brama, 1171, 1173
Brama japonica, 1171, 1172, 1173
Brama sp., 1170
BRAMIDAE, 1170
BRANCHIOSTEGIDAE, 531
Branchiostegus argentatus, 533
Branchiostegus japonicus, 532
Bream, 437
Bristle-tail filefish, 400
Brotula multibarbata, 1604
Brotulids, 997
Brown angelfish, 35
Brown-banded angelfish, 364
Brown-eared surgeonfish, 382
Brown flathead, 539
Brownspot cardinalfish, 241
Brownstripe wrasse, 130
Brown-striped blenny, 164
Bullseyes, 1254
Butterfish, 417
Butterfishes, 416, 1220
Butterfly-bream, 666, 1493
Butterflyfin lionfish, 512, 514
Butterflyfishes, 39, 743
Butterflymudskipper, 177

C
Caesio, 221, 673, 742
Caesio caerulaureus, 677, 1296
Caesio chrysozonus, 223, 1503
Caesio cuning, 1502
Caesio erythrogaster, 1872
Caesio pisang, 1503
Caesio pulcherrimus, 1505
Caesio xanthonotus, 676, 1294
CALLIONYMIDAE, 219
Callionymus, 219
Callionymus picturatus, 220
Callionymus richardsoni, 486
Callionymus splendidus, 220
Calliurichthys japonicus, 1330
Calloplesiops altivelis, 156, 224,
  1253
Callyodon improvisus, 630
Calotomus japonicus, 995
Calotomus spinidens, 631
Canary forktail blenny, 470
Cantherhines, 1905
Cantherhines dumerili, 1348
Cantherhines fronticinctus, 822
Cantherhines howensis, 1907
Cantherhines sandwichensis, 1354,
  1355

Canthidermis maculatus, **120, 1348**
Canthigaster, 823
Canthigaster bennetti, **402, 826, 827, 1360, 1635**
Canthigaster cinctus, **110, 111, 1359**
Canthigaster compressus, **1638**
Canthigaster jactator, **402**
Canthigaster janthinopterus, **823, 1361, 1634**
Canthigaster rivulatus, 98
Canthigaster solandri, 98, **402**
Canthigaster valentini, **401, 825, 1358, 1359, 1902**
CANTHIGASTERIDAE, 96, 823
Caprodon longimanus, **496**
Caprodon schlegeli, **496**
CARACANTHIDAE, 641
Caracanthus maculatus, **641**
CARANGIDAE, 423
Caranx armatus, **1055**
Caranx bucculentus, **1054**
Caranx delicatissimus, **431**
Caranx emburyi, **1807**
Caranx ferdu, **1809**
Caranx fulvoguttatus, **1808**
Caranx helvolus, **430**
Caranx ignobilis, **1806**
Caranx malabaricus, **1053**
Caranx melampygus, **1808**
Caranx sp., **431, 1055, 1806, 1809**
CARAPIDAE, 510
Carapus sp., **510**
CARCHARHINIDAE, 1087
Carcharodon carcharias, **1088**
Cardinalfishes, 240, 678, 1433, 1681, **1684**
Catsharks, 501, 1399, 1666
CENTRISCIDAE, 222, 319
Centriscus, 319
CENTROLOPHIDAE, 1220
Centrolophus, 1220
Centropholis petersi, **1171**
Centropyge, 7, 15, 21, 781
Centropyge acanthops, **780**
Centropyge bicolor, 26, **1133, 1540, 1541**
Centropyge bispinosus, **27, 365, 781, 1133**
Centropyge ferrugatus, **20, 21, 1129, 1130**
  Frontispiece Book 1, **1**
Centropyge fisheri, **365**
Centropyge flavissimus, 8, **18, 20,** 363, 781, **1543,** 1607
Centropyge heraldi, 8, **18, 19, 1131,** 1607
Centropyge loriculus, **22, 23, 24,** 781
Centropyge multifasciatus, **1542**
Centropyge multispinus, **782**
Centropyge nox, 362, **1134**
Centropyge potteri, **363**
Centropyge tibicen, **25,** 363, **1134, 1135**
Centropyge vroliki, 20, **85, 365, 1132, 1542,** 1607
Centropyge sp., **37**

Centrostephanus rodgersii, 1664
Cephalopholis, 252, 643
Cephalopholis argus, **499,** 642, **1237**
Cephalopholis aurantius, **1238, 1484, 1486**
Cephalopholis boenack, **492,** 644, **1236**
Cephalopholis coatesi, **1483**
Cephalopholis leopardus, 652, **1486**
Cephalopholis miniatus, **491, 492, 1485, 1487, 1839, 1844, 1845, 1855**
Cephalopholis pachycentron, **1237, 1489, 1851**
Cephalopholis rogaa, **646**
Cephalopholis urodelus, **500, 1239, 1485, 1842**
Cepola, 931
Cepola australis, **1888**
CEPOLIDAE, 931, 1888
Ceram wrasse, **147**
Chaenogobius urotaenia, **478**
Chaetoderma, 1905
Chaetoderma pencilligera, **398,** 1905
  (See *Chaetodermis spinosissimus*)
Chaetodermis spinosissimus, **398, 1352, 1358**
Chaetodipterus, **1139**
Chaetodon, 761
Chaetodon adiergastos, **57, 1191**
Chaetodon argentatus, **65, 1194**
Chaetodon aureofasciatus, **1774, 1779, 1780**
Chaetodon aureus, **40**
Chaetodon auriga, **54, 55,** 749, **1205,** 1767
Chaetodon baronessa, **1192, 1525, 1762**
Chaetodon bennetti, **48, 64, 379, 748, 1187**
Chaetodon "chrysurus," 750, 751
Chaetodon citrinellus, **72,** 376, **755, 1198, 1199, 1772**
Chaetodon daedalma, **53**
Chaetodon ephippium, **44, 46, 47, 49,** 375, **1179, 1520, 1521, 1766**
Chaetodon falcula, **52,** 759, 760, **761,** 765
Chaetodon flavirostris, 1520, **1524, 1547, 1781, 1782**
Chaetodon fremblii, **374**
Chaetodon guentheri, **65, 1199, 1171**
Chaetodon guttatissimus, 752, 753
Chaetodon kleini, **41,** 374, 743, 744, 745, **1196, 1197,** 1520, **1522, 1523, 1774**
Chaetodon lineolatus, **42, 379,** 764, 765, **1192, 1193,** 1763
Chaetodon lunula, **50, 51, 1188**
Chaetodon melannotus, **42,** 377, 752, **1182**
Chaetodon mertensi, **45, 63,** 1764
Chaetodon meyeri, **65,** 756, 757, 758
Chaetodon miliaris, **374**
Chaetodon modestus, **62, 1196**

Chaetodon multicinctus, **48**
Chaetodon nippon, **49, 66**
Chaetodon octofasciatus, **66, 372, 1186, 1187**
Chaetodon ornatissimus, **59, 64, 1181, 1520, 1521, 1783**
Chaetodon pelewensis, **1520, 1655, 1768, 1769**
Chaetodon pictus, **763**
Chaetodon plebeius, **64, 373, 379, 762, 1180, 1181, 1710, 1770**
Chaetodon punctatofasciatus, **53, 1195,** 1520
Chaetodon quadrimaculatus, **50**
Chaetodon rafflesi, **52, 1200, 1201**
Chaetodon rainfordi, **1776, 1777, 1778, 1779**
Chaetodon reticulatus, **43, 377, 1200**
Chaetodon semeion, **63,** 754, **1183,** 1767
Chaetodon speculum, **41, 43, 373, 1191, 1771**
Chaetodon strigangulus, **67**
Chaetodon tinkeri, **378**
Chaetodon triangulum, **57, 58, 378, 379,** 743
Chaetodon trifascialis, **45, 67, 380, 1202, 1524, 1766**
Chaetodon trifasciatus, **55, 60, 61,** 755, **1203, 1526, 1527, 1710, 1773**
Chaetodon ulietensis, **1204, 1205, 1528**
Chaetodon unimaculatus, **43, 1190, 1524, 1765**
Chaetodon vagabundus, **56,** 376, **1188,** 1520, **1527, 1764**
Chaetodon wiebeli, **67, 1185**
Chaetodon xanthocephalus, **743, 746, 747**
Chaetodon xanthurus, **63, 1184**
CHAETODONTIDAE, 39, 743, 1520
Chaetodontoplus, 781
Chaetodontoplus chrysocephalus, 8, **35**
Chaetodontoplus conspicillatus, **1784**
Chaetodontoplus duboulayi, **1121, 1785**
Chaetodontoplus melanosoma, 8, **35, 362, 1123**
Chaetodontoplus mesoleucus, **36, 37**
Chaetodontoplus personifer, **1121, 1122, 1123, 1786, 1787**
Chaetodontoplus septentrionalis, 8, **32, 33, 34, 1119, 1120**
CHANIDAE, 1044
Chanos chanos, **1044**
Chasmichthys dolichognathus, **178**
Chasmichthys gulosus, **178, 478**
Chaunax fimbriatus, **525, 1094**
Checkerboard wrasse, **147,** 454, **455, 605**
Cheilinus, 128, 569
Cheilinus bimaculatus, **573, 894**
Cheilinus ceramensis, **147**

Cheilinus chlorourus, **896, 1565, 1566**
Cheilinus diagrammus, **1567, 1568, 1733**
Cheilinus fasciatus, **446, 569, 570, 571**
Cheilinus oxycephalus, **894, 895**
Cheilinus rhodochrous, **895**
Cheilinus trilobatus, **572, 896, 898**
Cheilinus undulatus, **441, 574, 1566, 1732**
Cheilio inermis, **477, 592, 872, 873**
CHEILODACTYLIDAE, **251**
Cheilodactylus, **251**
Cheilodipterus, **678, 1432, 1681**
Cheilodipterus lachneri, **681, 686**
Cheilodipterus lineatus, **680, 681**
Cheilodipterus macrodon, **461, 966, 1432, 1433**
Cheilodipterus quinquelineatus, **1433, 1682**
Cheilodipterus zonatus, **1437**
Cheilodipterus sp., **1430**
Chelidonichthys kumu, **537**
Chelidoperca hirundinacea, **1226**
Chelmon, **761**
Chelmon marginalis, **1758, 1759**
Chelmon muelleri, **1760**
Chelmon rostratus, **38, 73, 371, 761, 1759**
Chelonodon, **1903**
Chelonodon patoca, **1903**
Chevron butterflyfish, **45**
Chilomycterus, **96**
Chiloscyllium colax, **502**
Chiloscyllium griseum, **1082**
Chiloscyllium indicum, **1083**
Chimaera phantasma, **1080**
Chinese sergeant-major, **195**
Choerodon, **1729**
Choerodon anchorago, **1735**
Choerodon azurio, **150, 451, 860**
Choerodon schoenleinii, **133, 859, 860, 1734**
Choerodon venustus, **1735**
Choerodon sp., **133, 149**
Chorinemus orientalis, **1056, 1057**
Chorinemus tolooparah, **1057**
Chromis, **717**
Chromis amboinensis, **1554**
Chromis analis, **196, 1553**
Chromis atripectoralis, **190, 1040, 1711, 1712**
Chromis atripes, **1556**
Chromis caeruleus, **190**
 (See *Chromis atripectoralis*)
Chromis caeruleus, **1040, 1710, 1712**
Chromis chrysurus, **1710**
Chromis dimidiatus, **207, 218**
Chromis lineatus, **1556**
Chromis lepidolepis, **1556**
Chromis margaritifer, **1039, 1554**
Chromis nitidus, **1708**
Chromis notatus, **207, 306, 1038**
Chromis opercularis, **1711**
Chromis richardsoni, **1039**

Chromis rollandi, **1557**
Chromis ternatensis, **718, 1709**
Chromis weberi, **1711**
Chromis xanthochir, **1038**
Chromis xanthurus, **1557**
Chromis sp., **700, 1561, 1563**
Chrysophrys auratus, **1316**
Chrysophrys major, **434, 437**
Cigar wrasse, **447, 592, 872**
Cinnamon flounder, **276**
Cirrhilabrus exquisitus, **581, 870**
Cirrhilabrus solorensis, **870, 1582, 1583**
Cirrhilabrus temmincki, **1582, 1730**
Cirrhilabrus sp., **871**
Cirrhitichthys, **660**
Cirrhitichthys aprinus, **157, 488, 1818, 1819**
Cirrhitichthys aureus, **158, 487**
Cirrhitichthys falco, **1143, 1620, 1819**
Cirrhitichthys oxycephalus, **158, 1619, 1621**
CIRRHITIDAE, **155, 660, 1113**
Cirrhitops, **663**
Cirrhitus pinnulatus, **1142, 1144**
Cirripectes, **636**
Cirripectes variolosus, **637**
Cirripectes sp., **1336, 1337**
Citron butterflyfish, **72, 376**
Citron goby, **479**
Cleaner wrasse, **39, 129, 159, 453, 1569**
Clingfishes, **1009**
CLINIDAE, **159, 636**
Clown anemonefish, **188**
Clownfish, **188**
Clown surgeonfish, **387**
Clown sweetlips, **225, 345, 346**
Clown triggerfish, **114, 115, 116, 123, 396, 814**
Clown wrasse, **140, 448, 576, 849**
Clupea pallasi, **315, 317**
CLUPEIDAE, **313**
Cobia, **1321, 1322**
Cockatiel wrasse, **892**
Cold porgy, **139**
Cololabias saira, **331**
Comet, **244, 1253**
Comet grouper, **261**
Conger eels, **260, 1399**
Conger japonicus, **352**
CONGRIDAE, **260, 1399**
CONGROGADIDAE, **638**
Convict surgeonfish, **793**
Convict tang, **90**
Convict worm-goby, **420**
Copperband butterflyfish, **371**
Coradion altivelis, **1525, 1761, 1762**
Coradion chrysozonus, **380**
Coradion fulvocinctus, **62**
Coral beauty, **27, 365**
Coral hogfish, **442, 590, 591**
Coral parrotfish, **458**
Coral spinefoot, **390**
Coreoperca kawamebari, **522, 1235**

Coris, **569**
Coris africana, **576, 578**
Coris aygula, **141, 575, 850, 851**
Coris caudimacula, **580**
Coris flavovittata, **448**
Coris formosa, **578, 579**
Coris gaimard, **140, 448, 576, 579, 848, 849**
Coris picta, **1730**
Coris rosea, **448**
Coris variegata, **441**
Coris venusta, **848**
Coris yamashiroi, **137**
Corniger, **230**
Coromandel grouper, **250, 253**
Coryphaena equiselis, **1260**
Coryphaena hippurus, **1260, 1261**
CORYPHAENIDAE, **1261**
Corythoichthys intestinalis, **699**
Cottogobius yongei, **476, 1807**
Croakers, **1319**
Cromileptes, **643**
Cromileptes altivelis, **252, 256, 527, 1849**
Crosshatch butterflyfish, **63**
Crosshatch triggerfish, **118**
Crowned blenny, **163, 471**
Crowned sea horse, **212**
Cryptocentrus sp., **1601**
Cryptocentrus filifer, **1601**
Cryptocentrus fontanesii, **1599**
Cryptocentrus koumansi, **1895**
Cryptocentrus sp., **1601**
Ctenochaetus, **803**
Ctenochaetus cyanoguttatus, **801, 1155**
Ctenochaetus striatus, **802, 803, 1607**
Ctenochaetus strigosus, **387, 801, 1147**
Ctenochaetus tominiensis, **1608**
Ctenogobius maculosus, **1896**
Ctenoscolopsis, **1493**
Ctenoscolopsis ciliatus, **1493, 1494**
Ctenotrypauchen microcephalus, **478**
Cusk-eels, **997**
Cutlassfishes, **927**
Cuvier's wrasse, **445**
Cynoscion macdonaldi, **1319**
Cypselurus opisthopus, **330**
Cypselurus pinnatibarbatus, **992**
Cypselurus poecilopterus, **922**
Cyprinocirrhites, **663, 1143**
Cyprinocirrhites polyactis, **1619, 1621**

D
DACTYLOPTERIDAE, **534**
Dactylopterus orientalis, **534**
Dactylopus, **219**
Daicocus peterseni, **535, 963**
Dampierosa, **959**
Damselfishes, **181, 289, 701, 1545**
Dascyllus, **181, 289, 290, 701**
Dascyllus albisella, **303**

Dascyllus aruanus, **202, 702, 738, 1022**
Dascyllus carneus, 701, **703**
Dascyllus marginatus, **198-199**
Dascyllus melanurus, **204, 1553**
Dascyllus reticulatus, **205,** 701, **703, 1022, 1706**
Dascyllus trimaculatus, **205, 303, 714, 1553, 1705, 1707**
Dascyllus sp., **661, 700**
Dash-dot cardinalfish, **463**
Dasson trossulus, **164**
    (See *Petroscirtes breviceps*)
DASYATIDAE, 509, 1393, 1673
Dasyatis, 1673
Dasyatis akajei, **509**
Dasyatis gerrardi, **1078**
Dasyatis sephen, 1673, **1675, 1676**
Datnioides, 1265
Decapterus, 423
Decapterus russellii, **1058**
Decorated triggerfish, **117, 394**
Dendrochirus, 258, 653
Dendrochirus brachypterus, **524, 653, 1828**
Dendrochirus zebra, **514, 659, 1827, 1829**
Dendrochirus zebra, **265**
    (See *Pterois antennata*)
Dendrochirus sp., **265**
Devil stinger, **515, 536**
Diademichthys, 1009
Diademichthys lineatus, **1590**
Diagram sweetlips, **224**
Diana wrasse, **131**
Diaphanous boxfish, **415**
Dicotylichthys myersi, **1904**
Dictyosoma burgeri, **170**
Dinematichthys, 997
Dinematichthys iluocoeteoides, **996, 1605**
Diodon, 96
Diodon holacanthus, **103**
Diodon hystrix, 96, **410, 411**
DIODONTIDAE, 96
Diplogrammus, 219
Diploprion bifasciatum, 252, 489, **492, 1228, 1229, 1836, 1837**
Diproctacanthus xanthurus, **447**
Ditrema temmincki, 335, **336, 337**
Dixie Reef, **1661**
Doderleina berycoides, **1230**
Dolphins, 1261
Doryrhamphus melanopleura, **213, 325, 1420**
Dotted butterflyfish, **63**
Dottybacks, 156
Double-ocellated scorpionfish, **524**
Double-saddle butterflyfish, **52**
Draculo, 219
Dragon fish, **218**
Dragonets, 219
Drepane, 1141
Drepane longimana, **1140**
Drepane punctata, **1141**
DREPANIDAE, 1138

Drepaninae, 1139
Drums, 1319
Dunckerocampus caulleryi, 1420
Dunckerocampus dactyliophorus, **325, 1420, 1421**
Dusky goby, **174, 478**
Dusky spinefoot, **388**

E
Eagle rays, 1074, 1672
ECHENEIDAE, 1803
Echeneis naucrates, **1803, 1804**
Echidna nebulosa, **353,** 1002, **1403**
Echidna zebra, **354,** 1403
Ecsenius, 636
Ecsenius collettei, **1597**
Ecsenius lineatus, **1336**
Ecsenius namiyei, **1592**
Ecsenius pulcher, **470**
Ecsenius yaeyamaensis, **1596, 1597**
Ecsenius sp., **1596**
Eight-banded butterflyfish, **66, 372**
Electric rays, 1067
Elegatis bipinnulatus, **1056**
ELEOTRIDAE, 172, 633
Eleotriodes, 633
Eleotriodes elapoides, **175, 474**
Eleotriodes longipinnis, **1894**
Eleotriodes strigatus, **474, 476, 632, 633, 1016, 1603**
Eleotriodes virgata, **171**
Eleotris fuscus, **1598**
Eleotris sp., **1598**
Eleutherochir, 219
Eleutheronema tetradactylum, **1175**
Elops machnata, **1042**
EMBIOTOCIDAE, 335
Emerald bass, **495**
Emperor angelfish, **8, 9, 10, 11, 12, 13, 688, 787**
Emperor bream, 663, 1880
Emperor snapper, 221, **674**
Engraulis japonica, **1045**
Entomacrodus, 636
Eopsetta grigorjewi, **276, 542**
EPHIPPIDAE, 1138
Ephippinae, 1138, 1139
Ephippus, 1139
Ephippus orbis, **1139**
Epibulus, 1729
Epibulus insidiator, **441, 887, 1576, 1577**
Epinephelus, 643, 652, 1839
Epinephelus akaara, **1242**
Epinephelus amblycephalus, **1246**
Epinephelus areolatus, **1802**
Epinephelus awoara, **1240**
Epinephelus caeruleopunctatus, **497, 1246, 1247**
Epinephelus cometae, **261, 1243**
Epinephelus coromandelicus, **250, 253**
Epinephelus damelii, 252
Epinephelus episticus, **1243**
Epinephelus fario, **254, 645, 1242, 1249, 1251, 1488**

Epinephelus fasciatomaculatus, **1240, 1241**
Epinephelus fasciatus, 643, **500, 1238, 1239, 1250, 1490, 1853**
Epinephelus flavocaeruleus, **494**
Epinephelus fuscoguttatus, **1852**
Epinephelus hexagonatus, **493, 1248**
Epinephelus kohleri, **261, 1852**
Epinephelus macrospilus, **1247**
Epinephelus megachir, **1249, 1250, 1849, 1850**
Epinephelus merra, **261, 493, 645, 1244, 1491, 1839, 1847, 1848**
Epinephelus moara, 252, **255, 1242**
Epinephelus rhyncholepis, **1241**
Epinephelus septemfasciatus, **498, 1243**
Epinephelus summana, **497**
Epinephelus tauvina, **493, 1244, 1245, 1840, 1846, 1847, 1856**
Epinephelus sp., **254, 1244**
Equetus, 1319
Equula, 1165
Erosa, 959
Erosa erosa, **961**
Escolars, 927
Etelis carbunculus, **1292**
Etrumeus micropus, **1045**
Eupomacentrus gascoynei, **1717**
Eupomacentrus nigricans, **1717**
Euthynnus affinis, **1325, 1327**
Euthynnus pelamis, **1325, 1329**
Euxiphipops, 786
Euxiphipops navarchus, **28, 29, 360, 361, 1534**
Euxiphipops sexstriatus, **16, 361, 1124, 1794, 1798**
Euxiphipops xanthometapon, **30, 31, 359, 783, 1535, 1539**
Eviota abax, **174**
Evistias acutirostris, 1217
Evynnis cardinalis, **1313**
Evynnis japonica, **1313, 1315**
Exallias, 636
Exallias brevis, **640**
EXOCOETIDAE, 328, 925

F
False cleaner, **471**
Fan bellied filefish, **400**
Fan-finned frogfish, **529**
Fanfishes, 1170, 1172
Fantailed filefish, **397**
Filament butterflyfish, **54, 55**
Filefishes, 122, 819, 1351, 1905
Firefish, **176**
Fisher's angelfish, **365**
Fishing frog, **528**
Fistularia petimba, **324, 1800**
Five-lined cardinalfish, **240**
Five-lined goby, **173, 479**
Flag-tailed rock cod, **500**
Flagtail, **791**
Flagtails, 308
Flaming angelfish, **22, 23, 24**
Flammeo, 230, 231, 689

Flammeo laeve, **693**
Flammeo operculare, **1452, 1453**
Flammeo sammara, 233, **1452, 1688,
1689**
Flathead, 538, **775**
Flyingfish, **330, 427**
Flyingfishes, 328, 925
Flying gurnards, 534
Foa, 1681
Fodifoa, 1681
Forcipiger, 743
Forcipiger flavissimus, 68, **370,** 743,
770, **1215, 1530, 1756, 1757**
Forcipiger longirostris, 743, **1757**
Forktail blenny, **163**
Formio, 1169
Four-lined wrasse, **449**
Four-spot butterflyfish, **50**
Fowleria, 678
Fowleria aurita, **684**
Foxface, **92**
Fox jacopever, **520**
Franzia fasciatus, **239**

G

Galeocerdo cuvieri, 1087, **1670,** 1672
Gaterin, 222
Gaterin albovittatus, 348, **1267,
1268**
Gaterin chaetodonoides, 89, 225,
228, 345, 346, **1269, 1506, 1507,
1509**
Gaterin cinctus, **349**
Gaterin diagrammus, **224**
Gaterin flavomaculatus, **1269**
Gaterin gaterinus, **670**
Gaterin goldmanni, **1511, 1877**
Gaterin orientalis, 347, 669, **671,
1271, 1272, 1274, 1275, 1506,
1508, 1510, 1877**
Gaterin picus, 228, **1273,** 1274, **1511**
Gaterin punctatissimus, 670, **1877,
1878, 1879**
Gaterin sp., **1270**
Gazza, 1165
GEMPYLIDAE, 927
Gempylus serpens, 929
Genicanthus, 7
Genicanthus fucosus, **17**
Genicanthus lamarck, 12, **19, 1544**
Genicanthus melanospilus, **1544,
1798**
Genicanthus semifasciatus, **19**
Genicanthus watanabei, 7, **17, 1128**
Gephyroberyx japonicus, **1161**
Gerres abbreviatus, **919**
Gerres baconensis, **918**
Gerres filamentosus, 917, **920**
Gerres oyena, **771**
GERRIDAE, 917
Ghost butterfish, **419**
Ghost pipefish, **216, 217**
Ghost pipefishes, 214
Giant wrasse, **441, 574**

Girdled sweetlips, **349**
Girella, 433
Girella punctatus, 433, **546**
Girella tricuspidata, 433
Glassfishes, **1430**
Glaucosoma fauveli, 1254, **1255**
Glaucosoma hebraicum, 1255
Glaucosoma magnificus, **1254**
Glaucosoma scapulare, 1161, 1255
GLAUCOSOMIDAE, 1254
Gnathagnus elongatus, **982**
Gnathanodon speciosus, **424, 425,**
1052
Gnathodentex, 666
Gnathodentex aurolineatus, **232,**
666, 667, **1500, 1617, 1886**
Goatfishes, 259, 739, 1461
Gobies, 172, **633**
GOBIESOCIDAE, 1009
Gobiesox, 1009
GOBIIDAE, 172, 633
Gobiodon, 172
Gobiodon citrinus, **479, 632, 1010**
Gobiodon quinquestrigatus, **173,**
479
Goggle-eye scad, **552**
Gold-bar snapper, **436**
Gold eye-band cardinalfish, **463**
Gold-striped butterfly bream, **439**
Gold-striped cardinalfish, **243**
Golden-banded goatfish, **342**
Golden butterflyfish, **40, 754**
Golden clingfish, **165**
Golden frogfish, **528**
Golden hawkfish, **158, 487**
Golden headed goby, **632**
Golden-headed sleeper, **474, 476**
Golden jack, **424, 425**
Golden-spot spinefoot, **94**
Golden-striped grouper, **256, 652**
Gomphosus, 1729
Gomphosus varius, **142, 143,** 577,
585, 586, **587, 852**
Goniistius, 251
Goniistius fuscus, 245, **246, 1811**
Goniistius gibbosus, 246, **251, 964,
1811**
Goniistius quadricornis, **247, 481,
964**
Goniistius zebra, **247**
Goniistius zonatus, 248, **249, 481,
964, 965**
Goosefishes, 508
Gorgasia maculata, **1401**
Grammistes sexlineatus, 256, **257,
652, 1227**
Grammistes sp., **256**
Grammistops ocellatus, **1482**
Gray puffer, **406**
Greasy grouper, **493**
Green clingfish, **165**
Green puffer, **405**
Greenling, **540, 541**
Groupers, 251, 489, 643, 1839, 1840
Grunions, 1412
Grunts, 222, 1507

Guitarfishes, 1073, 1677
Gymnapogon urospilotus, **1443**
Gymnocaesio, **1503**
Gymnocirrhites arcatus, **1820**
Gymnocranius audleyi, **1883**
Gymnocranius griseus, **1302, 1315**
Gymnocranius microdon, **1302**
Gymnothorax favagineus, 354, **1687**
Gymnothorax fimbriatus, **1002**
Gymnothorax flavimarginatus,
1000, 1407, 1686
Gymnothorax kidako, 274, **354**
Gymnothorax leucostigma, 274, **351**
Gymnothorax meleagris, **1000, 1408**
Gymnothorax pictus, **1001, 1402**
Gymnothorax thyrsoidea, **1406**
Gymnothorax undulatus, 354, **1001,
1407**
Gymnothorax xanthostomus, 353
Gymnothorax zonipectus, **350,** 1404
Gymnothorax sp., **1403, 1405, 1406,
1687**
Gymnura, 1673
Gymnura japonica, **505**
Gyropleurodus, 1664

H

Hairtail blenny, **466**
Halaelurus analis, **1081**
Half-and-half goatfish, **272**
Half-and-half wrasse, 145, **583**
Halfbeak, **331**
Halfbeaks, 925
Half-striped angelfish, **19**
Halichoeres, 601, 1729
Halichoeres argus, 455, **902**
Halichoeres bimaculatus, **600**
Halichoeres biocellatus, 454, **901**
Halichoeres centiquadrus, 147, 454,
455, 604, 605, 606, **607, 907, 908,
909, 1574, 1739**
Halichoeres hoeveni, **603**
Halichoeres kawarin, 610, **611, 906**
Halichoeres leparensis, **904**
Halichoeres margaritaceus, 455,
906, 907, 1575
Halichoeres marginatus, 143, **900,
901**
Halichoeres melanochir, 602, **910**
Halichoeres miniatus, **903**
Halichoeres nebulosus, **910**
Halichoeres nigrescens, **601**
Halichoeres notopsis, **603**
(= *Halichoeres marginatus*)
Halichoeres poecilopterus, 137, 451,
899
Halichoeres scapularis, 454, **608,
609, 905**
Halichoeres trimaculatus, **904**
Halieutaea fumosa, **526**
Halieutaea retifera, 525
Halieutaea stellata, **526**
(See *Halieutaea fumosa*)
Halieutaea stellata, **1092, 1093**
Haliophis guttatus, **638**
Halmablennius lineatus, **1338**

Halophryne diemensis, **1821**
Hammerhead sharks, 1087
Hapalogenys mucronatus, **1310**
Hapalogenys nigripinnis, **237, 1310**
Hardwicke's wrasse, **146**
Hardyheads, 1412
Harengula, **1413**
Harengula koningsbergeri, **1048**
Harlequin sweetlips, **345, 346**
Harlequin wrasse, **450, 451**
Harpadon microchir, **912**
Harpadon translucens, **912**
HARPADONTIDAE, 913
Hawaiian lionfish, **513**
Hawaiian squirrelfish, **340**
Hawaiian triggerfish, 114
Hawaiian turkeyfish, **524**
Hawkfishes, 155, 660, 1143
Helicolenus hilgendorfi, **268**
Helicolenus sp., **952**
Helotes, 1887
Helotes sexlineatus, 1887
Hemigymnus, 577
Hemigymnus fasciatus, **144, 582**
Hemigymnus melapterus, **145, 583,
584, 864, 1740**
Hemipteronotus pentadactylus,
446, 865
Hemipteronotus taeniourus, **445,
1568**
Hemipteronotus verrens, **865**
Hemipteronotus sp., **865**
Hemirhamphus commersoni, **1415**
Hemiramphus sajori, **331**
Hemiscyllium indicum, 1083
Hemiscyllium ocellatum, **1665, 1666**
Hemiscyllium trispeculare, 1666
Hemitaurichthys polylepis, **41, 1214**
Hemitaurichthys zoster, **768, 769**
Heniochus, 39, 75, 761
Heniochus acuminatus, **38, 39, 69,
75, 368, 369, 761, 1209, 1210,
1756**
Heniochus chrysostomus, **70, 1212,
1213, 1529, 1755, 1756**
Heniochus monoceros, **71, 72, 1210**
Heniochus permutatus, **70**
Heniochus pleurotaenia, **761, 766,
767**
Heniochus singularis, **70, 1210, 1211**
Heniochus varius, **70, 369, 767,
1206, 1207, 1208, 1754**
Herald's angelfish, 8, 18, 19
Heron Island, **1660**
Herrings, 313
HETERODONTIDAE, 504, 1664-
1665
Heterodontus, 1664
Heterodontus galeatus, **1664**
Heterodontus japonicus, **507**
Heterodontus zebra, **506, 1085, 1086**
Hexagrammos otakii, **540**
Hilu, **448**
Himantura, 1673
Hippocampus coronatus, **211, 212**
Hippocampus japonicus, **211**

Hippocampus kuda, **209, 211, 326**
Hippocampus mohnikei, **210**
Hippocampus sp., **214**
Hirundichthys oxycephalus, **923**
Histiopterus, 1217
Histiopterus acutirostris, **1216**, 1217
Histiopterus typus, **1216**
Histrio histrio, **259, 271, 1366**
Holacanthus, 7
Holacanthus arcuatus, **364**
Holacanthus trimaculatus, **27, 364**
Holacanthus venustus, **17**
HOLOCENTRIDAE, 230, 689
Holocentrus, 230, 689
Hologymnosus semidiscus, **145, 447,
592, 874, 875, 1728, 1729**
Holorhinus tobijei, **1076**
Holotrachys, 689
Honey jack, **430**
Honeycomb grouper, **493, 1244**
Hoplolatilus sp., **1590**
Hornfishes, 391
Hughichthys, 663
Humphead wrasse, **574**
Humuhumunukunuku-a-puaa, 114,
116
Hyperlophus, 1815
Hyperoglyphe, 1220
Hyperoglyphe japonica, 1220
Hypoatherina tsurugae, **316**
Hypseleotris guentheri, **1602**

I
Ichthyoscopus lebeck, **983**
Icichthys, 1220
Icichthys lockingtoni, **1220**
Indian little fish, **240, 462**
Indian wrasse, **445**
Indicus frogfish, **529**
Indigo wrasse, **443**
Iniistius dea, **450, 866**
Iniistius pavo, **132**
Inimicus didactylum, **268, 270**
  (See *Rhinopias argoliba*)
Inimicus japonicus, **515, 536**
Isobuna, 660
Istiblennius, 636
Istiblennius coronatus, **471**
Istiblennius edentulus, **1339**
Istiblennius lineatus, **1338**
Istiblennius meleagris, **1339**
Istiblennius sp., **1337**
ISTIOPHORIDAE, 1257
Istiophorus platypterus, **1259**

J
Jacks, 423
Jacopever, **520**
Japanese bigeye, **551, 552**
Japanese blanquillo, **532**
Japanese butterfly ray, **505**
Japanese butterflyfish, **66**
Japanese catshark, **503**
Japanese common eel, **351**
Japanese conger eel, **275, 352**
Japanese diamond skate, **505**
Japanese horse mackerel, **432**

Japanese parrotfish, **543, 544, 545**
Japanese puffer, **108**
Japanese sea horse, **211**
Japanese soldierfish, **229**
Japanese star-gazer, **541**
Japanese stingfish, **523**
Japanese stingray, **509**
Japanese swallow, **17**
Japanese wrasse, **130**
John Dory, **550**
Johnius, 1319
Julis musume, **133**

K
Kentrocapros aculeatus, **414**
Keyhole angelfish, **25, 363**
Kidako moray eel, **354**
Klein's butterflyfish, **41, 374**
Knifejaws, 543
Kohler's grouper, **261**
Koran angelfish, **14, 15, 366**
Kryptophanaron alfredi, **1411**
Kuhlia, 308
Kuhlia sandvicensis, 308
Kuhlia taeniura, **236, 308, 791**
KUHLIIDAE, 308
Kupipi, **194**
Kuweh, **430**
KYPHOSIDAE, 433, 1163
Kyphosus, 433, 1163
Kyphosus cinerascens, **237, 1162,
1163, 1835**
Kyphosus lembus, **1162**

L
Labracinus, 156
Labracinus cyclophthalmus, **156,
157, 1262, 1263**
Labracoglossa argentiventris, **419**
Labrichthys, 587
Labrichthys unilineata, **594, 595,
862**
LABRIDAE, 128, 569, 1729
Labroides, 39, 128, 587, 1800
Labroides bicolor, **136, 593, 861**
Labroides dimidiatus, **129, 136, 159,
255, 453, 651, 688, 861, 1487,
1545, 1580, 1581, 1687, 1800,
1839, 1875**
Labroides phthirophagus, **340**
Labroides sp. cf *phthirophagus*, **453**
Labropsis sp., **1581**
Lace-finned filefish, **117, 399**
Lactoria, 1899
Lactoria cornuta, **102, 413, 1364**
Lactoria diaphanus, **415**
Lactoria fornasina, **103**
Lactophrys, 1899
Lagocephalus lunaris, **405**
Lamarck's angelfish, **19**
Lampris regia, **323**
Lancetfishes, 1257
Lantern-eyes, 1411
Large-scale saury, **338**
Lateolabrax japonicus, **336, 1252**
Lates calcarifer, **1235**

Left-eyed flounders, 262
LEIOGNATHIDAE, 1165
Leiognathus, 1165
Leiognathus equulus, 1164
Leiognathus nuchilis, 236
Leiognathus rivulatus, 1164, 1166
Lemonpeel, 8, 20, 363
Leopard moray, 354
Leopard shark, 507
Leopard wrasse, 456
Lepadichthys frenatus, 165
Lepidotrigla microptera, 536, 1007
Lepidotrigla sp., 1008
Lepidozygus, 717
Lepidozygus anthioides, 716, 717
Leptocephalus, 260
Leptoscarus vaigiensis, 628, 993
Leptosynanceia, 959
LETHRINIDAE, 663, 666, 1880
Lethrinus choerorhynchus, 495
Lethrinus chrysostomus, 1514,
    1880, 1881, 1882
Lethrinus fletus, 1298, 1299
Lethrinus harak, 1301
Lethrinus kallopterus, 1300
Lethrinus leutjanus, 1300
Lethrinus miniatus, 1297
Lethrinus nebulosus, 1880, 1881
Lethrinus reticulatus, 418
Lethrinus variegatus, 1301
Lethrinus xanthocheilus, 1301
Lethrinus sp., 664, 1514, 1882, 1883
Lienardella fasciata, 450, 451, 879,
    1582, 1729, 1731
Limanda schrenki, 1097
Lined butterflyfish, 42, 379, 764
Lionfish, 258, 653
Liopropoma lineata, 1481
Liopropoma susumi, 1481
Liopropoma sp., 1480, 1481
LIPARIDAE, 168
Lizardfish, 719
Lizardfishes, 335
Lo, 1753
Lo vulpinus, 92, 93, 95, 1753
Loach gobies, 172
Lobotes pacificus, 1265
Lobotes surinamensis, 1265
LOBOTIDAE, 1265
Long-barbeled goatfish, 343
Long-finned batfish, 78, 79, 81
Long-finned caprodon, 496
Longhorned cowfish, 102, 413
Long-jawed squirrelfish, 234
Long-jawed wrasse, 441
Long-nosed butterflyfish, 68, 370,
    770
Lopez' unicornfish, 389
LOPHIIDAE, 508
Lophiomus setigerus, 508, 509
Lophonectes, 262
Lotella maximowiczi, 170
LUTJANIDAE, 221, 673
Lutjanus, 221, 629
Lutjanus amabilis, 1866
Lutjanus argentimaculatus, 1280,
    1869
Lutjanus bohar, 672, 1516, 1865
Lutjanus carponotatus, 1279, 1867
Lutjanus chrysotaenia, 226
Lutjanus erythropterus, 1284, 1285
Lutjanus flavipes, 1278
Lutjanus fulviflamma, 226, 1287,
    1288, 1289
Lutjanus gibbus, 672, 1277, 1518
Lutjanus janthinuropterus, 1283,
    1285
Lutjanus johni, 673, 1282, 1864,
    1865
Lutjanus kasmira, 221, 226, 227,
    1279, 1516, 1863
Lutjanus lineolatus, 1288
Lutjanus lutjanus, 1515
Lutjanus nematophorus, 221
Lutjanus quinquelineatus, 1278,
    1517, 1868
Lutjanus rivulatus, 1280
Lutjanus russelli, 1276
Lutjanus sanguineus, 672
Lutjanus sebae, 221, 674, 1518,
    1870, 1871
Lutjanus semicinctus, 1281
Lutjanus spilurus, 1278
Lutjanus superbus, 1286
Lutjanus vaigiensis, 1282
Lutjanus vitta, 436, 1289
Lutjanus sp., 226, 672, 1290
Lyretail coralfish, 489, 490
Lyretail wrasse, 457

M
Mackerels, 1325
Macolor niger, 349, 674, 1276
Macolor niger, 228
    (See *Gaterin picus*)
Macolor sp., 1519
Macropharyngodon meleagris, 877,
    878
Macropharyngodon pardalis, 456,
    876, 877
Macropharyngodon varialvus, 624
Macropharyngodon sp., 456, 878
MACRORHAMPHOSIDAE, 319
Macrorhamphosus scolopax, 322
Magpie morwong, 246, 251
Makaira indica, 1259
Makaira mazara, 1259
Makaira sp., 1805
Malacanthus latovittatus, 135, 531,
    1835
Malakichthys wakiyai, 1230
Malamaima, 448
Mandarin fish, 219, 482, 484, 485
Man-O-War fishes, 416
Manta birostris, 1397
Marine plotosid catfishes, 333
Marlins, 1257
Masked butterflyfish, 71, 72
Max's cod, 170
Megalaspis cordyla, 1058
MEGALOPIDAE, 1041
Megalops cyprinoides, 1041

Meiacanthus, 159, 1591
Meiacanthus atrodorsalis, 163, 470,
    1592, 1893
*Meiacanthus atrodorsalis oualanen-
    sis*, 470, 1593
Meiacanthus grammistes, 469, 1335,
    1594
Meiacanthus grammistes, 164
    (See *Meiacanthus kamoharai*)
Meiacanthus kamoharai, 164
Meiacanthus kamoharai, 469
    (See *Meiacanthus grammistes*)
Meiacanthus mossambicus, 469, 637
Meiacanthus sp., 1593
Melichthys, 815
Melichthys indicus, 397
Melichthys ringens, 397
    (See *Melichthys indicus*)
Melichthys vidua, 118, 120, 1628
Mempachi, 230
Mene maculata, 1167, 1168
MENIDAE, 1167
Merinthe macrocephalus, 953
Merten's butterflyfish, 63
Meuschenia skottowei, 121
Meyer's butterflyfish, 756, 758
Microcanthus strigatus, 74, 76, 480,
    1178
MICRODESMIDAE, 172, 633
Midnight angelfish, 362
Midshipmen, 1821
Milkfish, 1044
Milletseed butterflyfish, 374
Mimic blenny, 159
Minous monodactylus, 958
Minous versicolor, 958
Mirolabrichthys, 643
Mirolabrichthys dispar, 1472, 1473,
    1476
Mirolabrichthys evansi, 648, 650,
    651
Mirolabrichthys tuka, 422, 1383,
    1474, 1475
Mobula diabolus, 1075
MOBULIDAE, 1075
Mojarras, 917
MONACANTHIDAE, 122, 819,
    1351, 1905
Monacanthus chinensis, 400
Monacanthus filicauda, 1355, 1905
Monacanthus mosaicus, 399
Monkfishes, 1069
MONOCENTRIDAE, 260, 1889
Monocentris gloriamaris, 260, 1889
Monocentris japonica, 260, 273,
    1158, 1159
MONODACTYLIDAE, 74
Monodactylus argenteus, 74, 76, 312
Monodactylus sebae, 74
Monotaxis, 642, 664
Monotaxis grandoculis, 435, 662,
    663, 664, 665, 1500
Moonfishes, 74, 312, 1167
Moorish idol, 75, 77, 810
Moray eels, 260, 1403
MORINGUIDAE, 1410

Moringua microchir, **1409, 1410**
Morwongs, 251
Mosaic leatherjacket, 399
Mottled blenny, **472**
Mudskippers, 172
Mugil cephalus, **313, 314, 315, 316**
MUGILIDAE, 313
MUGILOIDIDAE, 777
Mullets, 313
MULLIDAE, 259, 739, 1461
Mulloidichthys, 259, 739
Mulloidichthys auriflamma, 342,
 980, 1460
Mulloidichthys pflugeri, **980**
Mulloidichthys samoensis, **739, 1461,
 1465**
Mullus, 259
Mullus surmuletus, 1461
Muraenesox cinereus, **351**
MURAENIDAE, 260, 1403
Mustard surgeonfish, **384**
Mylio latus, **437**
Mylio macrocephalus, 237, **438**
MYLIOBATIDAE, 1074, 1672
Myliobatus, 1672
Myliobatus tobijei, **1076**
Myripristis, 230, 689
Myripristis argyromus, **1064**
Myripristis bowditchae, **1064**
Myripristis kuntee, **233, 340**
Myripristis multiradiatus, **1694**
Myripristis murdjan, 230, 232, **1064,
 1694**
Myripristis pralinus, **341, 695, 1450**
Myripristis violaceus, **341, 694,
 1449, 1450**
Myripristis vittatus, **1449**
Myripristis sp., **231, 1617**

N
Narke japonica, **1067**
Naso, 84, 793
Naso brevirostris, **389, 807, 808,
 1153, 1154, 1612**
Naso lituratus, 89, 90, **390, 804, 805,
 806, 1155**
Naso lopezi, **389**
Naso unicornis, 89, **388, 807, 1152,
 1153, 1154**
Naso sp., **808**
Naucrates, 423
Naucrates ductor, **1059**
Navodon ayraud, **1356**
Navodon modestus, **126, 1352**
Needlefishes, 329
Nematalosa japonica, **1047**
Nemateleotris magnificus, 173, **176,
 1011**
Nemateleotris sp., **1603**
NEMIPTERIDAE, 666, 1493
Nemipterus, 666, 1493
Nemipterus bathybus, **439, 1294**
Nemipterus ovenii, **1303**
Nemipterus virgatus, **439, 1293**
Neoclinus bryope, **163**
Neoditrema ransonneti, 355, **337**

Neopercis aurantiaca, **467**
Neopercis multifasciatus, **468**
Neopercis sexfasciata, **468**
Network filefish, **127, 398, 408**
Nibblers, 433
Nibea albiflora, **1320**
Nibea goma, **1321**
Nibea mitsukurii, **1320**
Niphobles puffer, **113, 408**
Niphon spinosus, **544**
NOMEIDAE, 416, 1220
Nomeus gronovii, **417**
Novaculichthys taeniourus, **149**

O
Oblong filefish, 126
Oblong scorpionfish, 520
Oceanic sea horse, **211, 326**
Ocellate butterflyfish, **62, 65**
Ocycrius japonicus, **418**
Odonus niger, **119, 395, 1344**
OGCOCEPHALIDAE, 525
Omobranchus elegans, **162, 473**
One-band snapper, **436**
One-line rainbow wrasse, **135**
One Tree Island, **1661**
Onigocia spinosa, **539**
Opah, 323
OPHIDIIDAE, 997
Ophioblennius, 160
Ophiocara sp., **1598**
Opistognathus sp., **1401**
OPLEGNATHIDAE, 543
Oplegnathus fasciatus, **543, 544, 545**
Oplegnathus punctatus, **547**
Oplopomus sp., **1600**
Orange-finned anemonefish, **191**
Orange gurnard, **535**
Orange-ring batfish, 78, **80, 355**
Orbiculate cardinalfish, **243**
ORECTOLOBIDAE, 501, 1399,
 1666
Orectolobus, 1399
Orectolobus japonicus, **503,** 1082
Orectolobus ogilby, **501, 502,** 1666,
 1669
Orectolobus ornatus, 1666, **1667,
 1668**
Oriental sweetlips, **347**
Oriole angelfish, **26**
Ornate butterflyfish, **59, 64**
Ornate goby, **475**
Osbeckia, 1905
Ostichthys, 230, 689
Ostichthys japonicus, **229,** 230
Ostorhinchus angustatus, **687**
Ostorhinchus endekataenia, **686,
 687**
Ostorhinchus fleurieu, **966**
Ostorhinchus sp., **687**
Ostracion cubicus, **99, 100, 101,
 1362, 1638, 1898, 1899**
Ostracion meleagris, **101, 1364**
Ostracion tuberculatus, **1637**
OSTRACIONTIDAE, 97, 1899
Oval-spot butterflyfish, **41, 373**

Oxycirrhites, 660, 663, 1143
Oxycirrhites typus, 155, 660, **1619**
Oxymonacanthus, 821, 1905
Oxymonacanthus longirostris, **115,
 820, 821, 1633, 1904**
Oxyurichthys papuensis, **479**

P
Pacific hogfish, **143**
Paddlefin wrasse, **134**
Painted blenny, **166**
Painted coral bass, **490**
Painted sweetlips, **224**
Palani, **385**
Palau squirrelfish, **341**
Pampus, 1220
Pampus argenteus, **1219,** 1220
Pampus chinensis, 1220
Paopao, **424**
Papuan goby, **479**
Papirichthys pellucidus, **419**
 (See Psenes pellucidus)
Paracallionymus, 219
Paracanthurus, 797
Parachanthurus hepatus, 85, 87,
 281, 381, 1148, 1613
 Frontispiece (Book II), **1148,
 1613**
Paracentropogon longispinis, **517**
Paracentropogon rubripinnis, **518,
 536**
Paracentropogon vespa, **1823**
Parachaetodon ocellatus, **65**
Paracheilinus filamentosus, **1570,
 1571**
Paracirrhites, 155, 660
Paracirrhites arcatus, 155, 660, **661,
 1820**
Paracirrhites forsteri, **157, 1142,
 1618, 1620**
Paracirrhites typee, **488**
Paraglyphidodon melanopus, **1718**
 (Also known as Abudefduf
 melanopus)
Paraglyphidodon polyacanthus,
 1717, 1718, 1719
Paralichthys olivaceus, **1095**
Paraluteres, 821
Paraluteres prionurus, **401, 824,
 1353, 1635**
Paraluteres sp., **401**
Paramia quinquelineata, **240, 683**
Paramonacanthus barnardi, **822**
Paramonacanthus oblongus, **126**
PARAPERCIDAE, 467, 777
Parapercis, 777
Parapercis cephalopunctatus, **777,
 778, 779, 932**
Parapercis clathrata, **932, 1422**
Parapercis cylindrica, **776, 777, 932,
 1422, 1810**
Parapercis multifasciatus, **166**
Parapercis nebulosus, **933**
Parapercis pulchellus, **468, 473, 933**
Parapercis sexfasciatus, **167**
Parapercis tetracantha, **934, 1421**

Paraplagusia japonica, **1100**
Parapriacanthus, 251
Parapriacanthus dispar, **1418, 1419**
Parapristopoma, **1290**
Parapterurus heterurus, **948**
Parascorpaena, 653, **1626**
Parascorpaena aurita, **654**
Parascorpaena picta, **955**
Pardachirus pavoninus, **1816**
Paristiopterus, **1217**
Parma polylepis, **1716**
Parmaturus sp., **1091**
Parrotfishes, 151, 626
Parupeneus, 739
Parupeneus barberinoides, **272**, 343, 344
Parupeneus barberinus, **979, 1466**
Parupeneus bifasciatus, **1462, 1463, 1464**
Parupeneus chryseredros, **740, 975, 1465, 1466**
Parupeneus chrysopleuron, **972**
Parupeneus cyclostomas, 740, **974, 975**
Parupeneus fraterculus, **972, 973**
Parupeneus indicus, **978**
Parupeneus macronemus, 343, **741**
Parupeneus pleurospilus, **978**
Parupeneus pleurotaenia, **973**
Parupeneus trifasciatus, 272, 342, **976, 977**
Parupeneus sp., **1466**
Pastel razorfish, **450**
Pastinachus, 1673
Pataecus fronto, **962**
Peacock grouper, **499**
Peacock wrasse, 137, **451**
Pearlfishes, 510
Pearlscale razorfish, **149**
Pearl-scaled angelfish, 20, **365**
Pearly monocle-bream, **422**
Pegasus volitans, **218**
Pelates, 1887
Pelates quadrilineatus, **1317, 1887**
Pelecanichthys, 262
Pen shell pearlfish, **510**
PEMPHERIDAE, 245
Pempherids, 1695, 1814
Pempheris, 245, 251
Pempheris japonicus, **1221**
Pempheris klunzingeri, **1223**
Pempheris oualensis, 245, 487, **1233**
Pempheris schwenki, **698**
Pempheris vanicolensis, **1418**
Pempheris xanthoptera, **244**
Pempheris sp., **487**
Pennant butterflyfish, 69, **368, 369**
Pentaceropsis, **1217**
Pentaceros, 1217
Pentaceros japonicus, **1217, 1218**
PENTACEROTIDAE, 1217
PENTAPODIDAE, 666
Pentapodus caninus, **1308, 1501**
Pentapodus nemurus, **1501**
Pentapodus setosus, **1886**
Peprilus, 1220

Percanthias japonicus, **1224**
Periophthalmus, 172
Periophthalmus cantonensis, **177**
Periophthalmus papilio, **177**
Peristedion nierstraszi, **1006**
Pervagor, 821
Pervagor melanocephalus, **117, 399, 1353, 1631**
Pervagor spilosoma, **397**
Pervagor tomentosus, **400**
Petrocheilops sp., **1601**
Petroscirtes, 636
Petroscirtes breviceps, **164, 1333**
Petroscirtes mitratus, **639**
Petroscirtes sp., **1891**
Philippine butterflyfish, **57**
Pholidichthys leucotaenia, **164, 420, 1428**
Photoblepharon palpebratus, **1411**
Pinecone fishes, 260, 273, **1889**
Pink-barred weever, **467**
Pink-tailed triggerfish, **118, 120**
Pipefishes, 208, 1420
Plagiotremus rhinorhynchos, **160, 161, 1591, 1594, 1892**
Plagiotremus tapeinosoma, **471, 1891, 1893**
Plagiotremus sp., **636**
PLATACIDAE, 78, 1138
Platacinae, 1138, 1141
Platax batavianus, 78, **1812**
Platax orbicularis, 78, 82, 83, **356, 357, 358, 1136, 1137**
Platax pinnatus, 78, 80, **355, 1531, 1533, 1812**
Platax teira, 78, **79, 81, 1138, 1532, 1813**
Platax sp., **1813**
Platichthys stellatus, 263
PLATYCEPHALIDAE, 538
Platycephalus crocodilus, **541, 1006**
Platycephalus indicus, **1004**
Platycephalus grandidieri, **775**
Platycephalus sp., **775**
Platyrhina sinensis, **1077**
Plectroglyphidodon johnstonianus, **1716** (Also known as *Abudefduf johnstonianus*)
Plectropomus, 643
Plectropomus leopardus, **1232, 1488**
Plectropomus maculatus, **1232, 1233, 1838, 1839, 1840, 1841, 1843**
Plectropomus oligacanthus, **1483**
Plectrypops, 230
PLESIOPIDAE, 156
Plesiops coeruleolineatus, **1480**
Pleurogrammus azonus, **541**
PLEURONECTIDAE, 262
Pleuronichthys cornutus, **1097**
PLOTOSIDAE, 333
Plotosus, 333
Plotosus anguillaris, 271, **333, 334, 1428, 1429**
Poecilopora, 641
Pogonoculius zebra, **179, 472, 1012**

Polkadot grouper, **256, 527**
Polymixia, 1173
Polymixia japonica, 1173, **1174**
Polymixia lowei, 1173
Polymixia nobilis, 1173
POLYMIXIIDAE, 1173
POMACANTHIDAE, 7, 781
Pomacanthus, 7, 781
Pomacanthus annularis, **26, 367**
Pomacanthus imperator, 8, 9, **10, 11, 12, 13, 786, 787, 788, 1114, 1115, 1116, 1117, 1538, 1539, 1794, 1795**
Pomacanthus semicirculatus, 12, **14, 15, 366, 1117, 1118, 1536, 1537, 1539, 1788, 1789, 1790, 1791, 1792, 1793**
POMACENTRIDAE, 181, 289, 701, 1545
Pomacentrus alexanderae, **1563**
Pomacentrus amboinensis, 201, 305, **1030, 1710, 1720**
Pomacentrus australis, **1721**
Pomacentrus azysron, **1727**
Pomacentrus bankanensis, **1028, 1029, 1559**
Pomacentrus coelestis, 197, 203, **1555, 1562**
Pomacentrus dorsalis, 201, **1027**
Pomacentrus flavicauda, **1725**
Pomacentrus lepidogenys, **1563, 1724, 1726**
Pomacentrus melanochir, **726, 1724**
Pomacentrus moluccensis, **201** (See *Pomacentrus amboinensis*)
Pomacentrus nigricans, 719, 720, 774
Pomacentrus nigromarginatus, **1560**
Pomacentrus notophthalmus, **1557, 1722**
Pomacentrus pavo, 725, **1027, 1725**
Pomacentrus perspicillatus, **1560**
Pomacentrus philippinus, **1726**
Pomacentrus popei, **1032, 1554**
Pomacentrus prosopotaenia, **1723**
Pomacentrus pseudochrysopoecilus, **1722, 1723**
Pomacentrus pulcherrimus, **726**
Pomacentrus reidi, **1562**
Pomacentrus sufflavus, **1026**
Pomacentrus taeniurus, **724, 725**
Pomacentrus trichourus, **721**
Pomacentrus tripunctatus, **722, 723**
Pomacentrus vaiuli, **304, 1725**
Pomacentrus wardi, **1722**
Pomacentrus sp., **206** (See *Abudefduf cyaneus*)
Pomacentrus sp., **1033**
POMADASYIDAE, 222, 666, 1507
Pomadasys hasta, **1311**
Pomadasys maculatus, **1311**
POMATOMIDAE, 1266
Pomatomus saltatrix, **1266**
Pomfrets, 416, 1170, 1220
Pompanos, 423
Ponyfish, 1165

Popeyed sea goblin, **268**
Porcupinefish, **410, 411**
Porcupinefishes, 96
Porgies, 433
Porky, **127**
Port and starboard light fish, 260
Port Jackson sharks, 504, 1664, 1665
Portuguese man-o-war fish, **417**
Powder-blue surgeonfish, **85, 381**
Praealticus, 1337
Pranesus ogilbyi, **1814**
Pranesus pinguis, **1412**
Premnas biaculeatus, **190, 301, 1389**, 1545, **1546, 1547**
PRIACANTHIDAE, 231, 551
Priacanthus cruentatus, **231, 1065, 1068**
Priacanthus hamrur, **552, 696, 697**
Priacanthus macracanthus, **248**
Priacanthus sp., **1458**
Prickly leatherjacket, **398**
Prionurus, 84, 797
Prionurus microlepidotus, **88**
Pristiapogon snyderi, **685**
Pristigenys niphonius, **551, 552, 1065**
Pristiophorus japonicus, **1079**
Pristipomoides argyrogrammicus, **1291**
Pristipomoides filamentosus, **1292**
Pristis cuspidatus, **1079**
Prometheichthys prometheus, **929**
Protoxotes, 328
Psenes indicus, **1221**
Psenes pellucidus, **419, 1221**
Psenopsis, 1220
Psenopsis anomala, **417**, 1220
Psettodes erumei, **1096**
Pseudamia, 1432
Pseudamia gelatinosa, **1439**
Pseudanthias taira, **239**
Pseudobalistes, 815
Pseudobalistes fuscus, **117, 125, 394, 1343**
Pseudoblennius cottoides, **166**
Pseudoblennius percoides, **166**
Pseudocheilinus evanidus, **456, 1579**
Pseudocheilinus hexataenia, **449, 625, 853, 1579**
Pseudocheilinus octotaenia, **449**
Pseudocheilinus tetrataenia, **449**
Pseudocheilinus sp., **625**
PSEUDOCHROMIDAE, 156
Pseudochromis, 156
Pseudochromis aureus, **1264**
Pseudochromis cyanotaenia, **1264**
Pseudochromis fuscus, **1477**
Pseudochromis melanotaenia, **1262, 1264**
Pseudochromis paccagnellae, **1478, 1479, 1862**
Pseudochromis xanthochir, **1478**
Pseudodax moluccanus, **443, 1569**
Pseudogramma polyacantha, **1482**
Pseudolabrus gracilis, **130**

Pseudolabrus japonicus, **130, 878, 896, 897**
Pseudoplesiops sargeanti, **1480**
Pseudopristipoma nigra, **1272**
Pseudorhombus cinnamoneus, **276**
Pseudupeneus, 259, 739
Pseudupeneus chryseredros, **740**
Pseudupeneus cyclostomas, **740**
Pseudupeneus macronema, **741**
    (These *Pseudupeneus* species are now considered under *Parupeneus*)
Psychedelic fish, **220, 483, 484**
PTERACLIDAE, 1173
Pteragogus flagellifera, **132, 148, 892, 893**
Pteragogus sp., **132**
Ptereleotris microlepis, **477**
Ptereleotris tricolor, **476, 477, 1012, 1013**
Ptereleotris splendidum, **173, 176**
    (See *Nemateleotris magnificus*)
Pterocaesio diagramma, **1296, 1872, 1873**
Pterocaesio tile, **676, 1295, 1502, 1504**
Pterogobius zonoleucus, **179**
Pterois, 258, 653
Pterois antennata, **263, 265, 657, 658, 944, 1829, 1830, 1831**
Pterois lunulata, **264, 512, 514, 938, 939, 1833**
Pterois radiata, **513, 944, 1622**
Pterois sphex, **513**
Pterois volitans, **265, 512, 940, 941, 942, 943, 1622, 1623, 1828, 1832, 1834**
Pterothrissus gissu, **1043**
Puffers, 94, 114, 1903
Purple flying gurnard, **534**
Purple queen, **422**
Purple surgeonfish, **384**
Pygoplites, 786
Pygoplites diacanthus, **24, 25, 789, 790, 1125, 1534, 1537, 1796, 1797**

Q
Quinquarius japonicus, 1217

R
Rabbitfishes, 93, 1753
Raccoon butterflyfish, **50, 51**
RACHYCENTRIDAE, 1323
Rachycentron canadum, **1322, 1323**
Raffles' butterflyfish, **52**
Rainbow wrasse, **612**
Razorfish, 319, 320, 321, 866
Razor-trevally, 1167
Rectangle triggerfish, **117, 394**
Red clownfish, **184, 187**
Red grouper, **491, 492**
Red gurnard, **537**
Red morwong, **245, 246**
Red parrotfish, **459**
Red rattlefish, **526**
Red-shoulder wrasse, **131, 452**

Red soldierfish, **341**
Red-spotted grouper, **491**
Red-spotted razorfish, **446**
Red-striped wrasse, **133**
Red-tailed wrasse, **440**
Red-tooth triggerfish, **119, 395**
Red wasp-fish, **518, 536**
Reef stonefish, **521**
Regal angelfish, **24, 25, 790**
Remora albescens, **935**
Remora sp., **236**
Remoras, 1803
Requiem sharks, 1087
Reticulated butterflyfish, **43, 377**
Reticulated damselfish, **205**
Reticulated puffer, **105, 407**
Reticulated wrasse, **456**
Rhabdosargus sarba, **1314**
Rhina, 1677
Rhina ancylostomus, **1072, 1073, 1677**
Rhinchichthys, 230
Rhinecanthus, 815
Rhinecanthus aculeatus, **116, 817, 1346, 1628, 1629**
Rhinecanthus assasi, **125**
    (See *Rhinecanthus verrucosus*)
Rhinecanthus rectangulus, **117, 394, 1347**
Rhinecanthus verrucosus, **125, 1348**
RHINOBATIDAE, 1073, 1677
Rhinobatos, 1677
Rhinobatos armatus, **1677**
Rhinobatos formosensis, **1071**
Rhinobatos hynnicephalus, **1071**
Rhinogobius brunneus, **1015**
Rhinomuraena amboinensis, **275, 350, 998**
Rhinomuraena quaesita, **275, 999, 1409**
Rhinopias argoliba, **268, 270**
Rhinoplagusia japonica, **1100**
Rhinoptera, 1672
Rhynchobatus, 1677
Rhynchocymba nystromi, **352**
Rhyncostracion, 1899
Richardson's dragonet, **486**
Right-eyed flounders, 262
Rock blenny, **470**
Rouge fish, **517**
Round batfish, **82, 83, 356, 357, 358**
Ruby scat, **310**
Rudarius ercodes, **127, 398, 408**
Rudderfish, **429, 432**
Rudderfishes, 433, 1163
Russet angelfish, **363**
Rusty angelfish, **1, 20, 21**
Ruvettus pretiosus, **929**

S
Sabre-tooth blenny, **161, 471**
Sacura margaritacea, **238, 1225**
Saddle butterflyfish, **44, 46, 47, 49, 375**
Saddle-back clownfish, **183**
Saddled filefish, **401**

1922

Saddled puffer, **401**
Saddled rainbow wrasse, **455**
Sagamia genionema, 178, **478**
Sailfin leaffish, **516**
Sailfin tang, **89, 91**
Sailfishes, 1257
Salarias, 636
Salarias fasciatus, **639, 1336**
Salarius lineatus, **1338**
Salmonet, **272**
Samaris cristatus, **1098**
Sandsmelt, **236**
Sarda orientalis, **1326**
Sardinella, **1413**
Sardinella aurita, **1046**
Sardinella sp., **1046**
Sardines, 313
Sardinops melanosticta, **315, 317**
Sargassum fish, 259, **271**
Saurida, 335
Saurida gracilis, **916, 1427**
Saurida undosquamis, **338**
Saury, **331**
Sawtooth boxfish, **441**
Sayonara satsumae, **1226**
Scaled blennies, 159
Scaleless blennies, 159
SCARIDAE, 151, 626
Scarlet anglerfish, **528**
Scarlet wrasse, **456**
Scarops rubrioviolaceus, **986, 987, 1584, 1587**
Scarus aeruginosus, **989**
Scarus bowersi, **988**
Scarus capristratoides, **988**
Scarus chlorodon, **630**
Scarus dubius, **989**
Scarus erythrodon, **1587**
Scarus fasciatus, **1588**
Scarus frenatus, 665, **993, 1743**
Scarus ghobban, 153, 154, **990, 991, 992, 1741, 1742**
Scarus harid, **995**
Scarus janthochir, **988**
Scarus lepidus, 627, 927, **994**
Scarus madagascariensis, **629**
Scarus microrhinos, 154, **987**
Scarus mus, **1589**
Scarus niger, **1741**
Scarus sexvittatus, 152, 626, **627**
Scarus troscheli, **1584, 1585**
Scarus venosus, **458**
Scarus sp., 153, **459, 631, 992, 994**
SCATOPHAGIDAE, 309
Scatophagus, 309
Scatophagus argus, **309, 310, 311, 1176, 1177**
Scatophagus rubrifrons, 310, **1176**
Scats, 309, **312**
Schedophilus, 1220
Schedophilus maculatus, 1220
Schlegel's caprodon, **496**
SCIAENIDAE, 1319
Scissortail, **476, 477**
Scolopsis, 666, 1493, **1501**
Scolopsis bilineatus, 222, **223, 421,**

668, 1309, 1493, **1495, 1497, 1499, 1884**
Scolopsis cancellatus, 1303, **1309, 1496, 1498**
Scolopsis dubiosus, **421**
Scolopsis ghanam, **668**
Scolopsis margaritifer, **422, 1496, 1497, 1498, 1885**
Scolopsis monogramma, 1304, **1305, 1306**
Scolopsis temporalis, **1884**
Scolopsis vosmeri, **1307, 1308**
Scolopsis xenochrous, **1497, 1499**
Scomber, 1325
Scomber japonicus, **1327**
Scomberomorus commerson, **1328**
Scomberomorus koreanus, **1328**
Scomberomorus niphonius, **1328**
Scomberomorus sinensis, **1328**
SCOMBRIDAE, 1325
Scombrops boops, **548**
Scorpaena izensis, **950, 951**
Scorpaena neglecta, 268, 270, **949, 1822**
Scorpaena sp., **1822, 1823**
SCORPAENIDAE, 258, 511, **653, 959**
Scorpaenodes, 653
Scorpaenodes guamensis, **518, 957**
Scorpaenodes hirsutus, **1625**
Scorpaenodes littoralis, **957**
Scorpaenodes parvipinnis, **516**
Scorpaenopsis cirrhosa, 268, **655, 952, 1626, 1822, 1824**
Scorpaena gibbosa, **656, 948**
Scorpaenopsis sp., **1626**
SCORPIDIDAE, 74
Scorpionfishes, 266, **269**
Scorpionfishes, 258, 511, 653, 959
Scorpionopsis, 653
Sea-bull, **70, 369**
Sea horses, 208, 1420
Sea robins, 511
Sebastapistes, 653
Sebastapistes kowiensis, **656**
Sebastapistes oglinus, **655**
Sebastapistes sp., **1625**
Sebastes baramenuke, **954**
Sebastes inermis, **523**
Sebastes joyneri, 519, **523**
Sebastes matsubarai, **954**
Sebastes nivosus, 519, **522**
Sebastes oblongus, 520, **955**
Sebastes pachycephalus, **956**
Sebastes schlegeli, **520**
Sebastes trivittatus, **522**
Sebastes vulpes, **520**
Sebasticus marmoratus, 266, **267**
Sebasticus sp., **956**
Sebastolobus macrochir, **518**
Secutor, 1165
Secutor ruconius, **1165**
Selenotoca, 309
Semicossyphus reticulatus, 138, **139, 911**
Sergeant-major, **195**

Seriola aureovittata, **429**
Seriola dumerilii, **1059**
Seriola grandis, **1805**
Seriola nigrofasciata, **1060**
Seriola purpurascens, 429, 432, **1059**
Seriola quinqueradiata, **427, 428**
Seriolella, 1220
SERRANIDAE, 251, 489, **643, 1839, 1840**
Serranocirrhitus, 660
Setipinna breviceps, **1049**
Sharp-nosed puffers, 96, 98, **823**
Short-nosed unicornfish, **389**
Short-snouted tripodfish, **392**
Short-spined scorpionfish, **516**
Shovel-nosed rays, **1073**, 1677
Shrimpfish, 319, **320, 321, 1416, 1417**
Sicyopterus cf. *longifilis*, **1600**
Siderea picta, **1402**
SIGANIDAE, 93, 1753
Siganus, 1753
Siganus corallinus, **390**
Siganus doliatus, **1616**
Siganus fuscascens, **388**
Siganus lineatus, 94, **1615**
Siganus oramin, **95, 1145, 1614**
Siganus puellus, **1146, 1614, 1752**
Siganus rivulatus, 1753
Siganus rostratus, **1146**
Siganus spinus, **1145**
Siganus stellatus, **809**
Siganus striolata, **1145**
Siganus vermiculatus, **389**
Siganus virgatus, 93, **94, 1753**
Siganus vulpinus, 1753
Siganus sp., **1616**
Silky goby, **179**
SILLAGINIDAE, 1003
Sillago sihama, 236, **1003**
Silver blanquillo, **533**
Silver conger eel, **352**
Silver squirrelfish, **339**
Silver sweeper, 245, **487**
Silversides, 1412
Singular butterflyfish, **70**
Siphamia, 241, 1681
Six-banded perch, **167**
Six-banded weever, **468**
Six-lined wrasse, **449**
Six-striped angelfish, **16, 361**
Skipper, **174**
Skunk blenny, **170**
Skunk clownfish, **185, 188**
Sleeper gobies, 172, 633
Slipmouths, 1165
Smooth dogfishes, 504
Smoothhead unicornfish, 89, **90, 390**
Snake eels, 262
Snake mackerels, 927
Snakefish, **336**
Snakeskin goby, **178**
Snappers, 221, 673
Snipefishes, 319
Snowflake moray eel, **353**
Snowfleck scorpionfish, **519, 522**

Soapy, **236**
Solander's sharpnosed puffer, **402**
SOLEIDAÉ, 1099
Solenichthys sp., **215**
SOLENOSTOMIDAE, 214
Solenostomus, 214
Solenostomus paeginius, **216, 217**
Soles, 1099
Spadefishes, 1138
Spaghetti eels, 1410
SPARIDAE, 433
Spearfishes, 1257
Speckled-fin flathead, **539**
Speckled-finned grouper, **497**
Speckled wrasse, **131, 452**
Sphaeramia nematoptera, **243, 464,**
465, 1432, 1448
Sphaeramia orbicularis, **969, 1432,**
1448
Sphoeroides, **97, 1903**
Sphoeroides hamiltoni, **1900**
Sphoeroides pleurogramma, **1903**
Sphoeroides pleurostictus, **1903**
Sphoeroides squamicauda, **1903**
Sphoeroides tuberculiferus, **1903**
Sphoeroides whitleyi, **1903**
Sphyraena barracuda, **318, 921**
Sphyraena japonica, **698**
Sphyraena pinguis, **318**
Sphyraena qenie, **921**
Sphyraena sp., **1414**
SPHYRAENIDAE, 925
Sphyrna blochii, **1090**
Sphyrna corona, **1090**
Sphyrna couardi, **1090**
Sphyrna lewini, **1090**
Sphyrna media, **1090**
Sphyrna mokarran, **1090**
Sphyrna tiburo, **1090**
Sphyrna tudes, **1090**
Sphyrna zygaena, **1089, 1090, 1091**
SPHYRNIDAE, 1087
Spikefishes, 391
Spilotichthys pictus, **224, 348, 1268,**
1270, 1512, 1513, 1871, 1874,
1875, 1876, 1879
Spine-cheeked anemonefish, **190**
Spine-cheeked snapper, **222**
Spiny-eyed cardinalfish, **460**
Spiny puffer, **103**
Spiny-tailed tang, **88**
Spot-banded butterflyfish, **53**
Spot bream, **667**
Spotfin lionfish, **263**
Spottail wrasse, **580**
Spot-tailed cardinalfish, **461**
Spotted boxfish, **99**
Spotted grouper, **254, 645**
Spotted halibut, **276**
Spotted hawkfish, **157**
Spotted knifejaw, **547**
Spotted rabbitfish, **95, 809**
Spotted scat, **309**
Spotted sharpnosed puffer, **402**
Spotted triggerfish, **120**
Spotted wrasse, **442**

Spottyback scorpionfish, **519, 523**
Springeratus xanthosoma, **1334**
Spur Reef, **1662, 1663, 1783**
Squatina japonica, **1070**
SQUATINIDAE, 1069
Squirrelfishes, 230, 689
Stanulus seychellensis, **472**
Stargazers, 538
Starry flounder, 263
Starry triggerfish, **395**
Stegostoma fasciatum, **1084, 1398,**
1399
Stephanolepis cirrhifer, **127, 1354**
Stereolepis ishinagi, 252, **541, 1234**
Stethojulis, 598
Stethojulis albovittata, **599**
Stethojulis axillaris, **131, 146, 452,**
598, **890**
Stethojulis bandanensis, **1738**
Stethojulis interrupta, **890, 891**
Stethojulis kalosoma, **135**
Stethojulis phekadopleura, **889**
Stethojulis strigiventer, **596, 597**
Stethojulis trilineata, **889, 891**
Stichaeus grigorjewi, **466**
Stigmatogobius javanicus, **1599**
Stingaree, **509**
Stingrays, 509, 1393
Stonefish, **521**
Stretched silk goby, **175, 474**
Striped-belly puffer, **106, 107, 109**
Striped cardinalfish, **460**
Striped catfish, **271, 333, 334**
Striped goby, **174**
Striped grouper, **451**
Striped grunter, **229**
Striped jack, **431**
Striped morwong, **248, 249, 481**
Stripey, **74, 76, 480**
STROMATEIDAE, 416, 1220
Stromateus, 1220
Strophiurichthys robustus, **1899**
Suckerfishes, 1803
Sufflamen, 815
Sufflamen bursa, **816, 1627**
Sufflamen chrysoptera, **120, 1628,**
1629
Sufflamen fraenatus, **120**
Sufflamen sp., **120**
Suggrundus meerdervoorti, **539,**
1005
Suggrundus sp., **1004, 1005**
Surfperch, **337**
Surfperches, 335
Surgeonfishes, 84, 793, 1607
Sweepers, 245
Sweeps, 74
Sweetlips, 222, 1507
Swordfish, 1260
Symphorichthys spilurus, **227**
Symphorus nematophorus, **227,**
1871
Synagrops, 678, 1432
Synanceia, 959
Synanceia horrida, **521**
Synanceia verrucosa, **521, 959, 960,**

1825, 1826
Synchiropus, 219, 220
Synchiropus lineolatus, **1331**
Synchiropus picturatus, 219, **220,**
483, 484
Synchiropus splendidus, 219, **220,**
482, 484, 485
Synchiropus sp., **218, 1331, 1332**
SYNGNATHIDAE, 208, 1420
Syngnathus schlegeli, **324**
SYNODONTIDAE, 335
Synodus, 335
Synodus indicus, **774**
Synodus variegatus, **338, 915, 1424,**
1425, 1426, 1427

T
Taenioconger hassi, **1400**
Taenionotus triacanthus, **516, 1624**
Taeniura, 1673
Taeniura lymma, **509, 1392, 1393,**
1673, **1674**
Tahitian squirrelfish, **339**
Tail-light damselfish, **207**
Taius tumifrons, **438**
Taractes, 1173
Taractes longipinnis, **1172**
Tarpons, 1041
Tasselled wobbegong, **501, 502**
Tawny wrasse, **150**
Teardrop butterflyfish, **43**
TETRAGONURIDAE, 1220
Tetraodon, 97
TETRAODONTIDAE, 97, 1903
Tetrapterus audax, **1258**
Tetrosomus gibbosus, **412, 415**
Thalassoma, 618
Thalassoma amblycephalus, **134,**
612, 614, 888, 889
Thalassoma fuscum, **885**
Thalassoma hardwicke, **146, 616,**
617, 618, 619, 880, 881, 1575
Thalassoma hebraicum, **457, 613**
Thalassoma janseni, **622, 886, 1740**
Thalassoma lunare, **457, 614, 615,**
1572, 1729
Thalassoma lutescens, **148, 149,**
882, 883, 884, 1572, 1573
Thalassoma quinquevittata, **620,**
885, 886
Thalassoma umbrostygma, **621, 886**
Therapon, 1887
Therapon jarbua, 222, **1318, 1887**
Therapon oxyrhinchus, **228**
Therapon theraps, 222, **229, 1318**
THERAPONIDAE, 222, 1887
Thick-lipped blenny, **166**
Thick-lipped goby, **178**
Tholichthys, 39
Thornback cowfish, **103**
Thornbacked boxfish, **412, 415**
Threadfin, **426**
Threadfin cardinalfish, **460**
Thread-sail fishes, **913**
Three-bar goatfish, **342**
Three-lined wrasse, **891**

Three-spot angelfish, **27, 364**
Three-spot damselfish, **205**
Three-striped butterflyfish, **60, 61**
Three-striped tigerfish, 222
Thrissa hamiltoni, **1048**
Thrush eels, 1410
Thunnus alalunga, **1324**
Thunnus obesus, **1324**
Thunnus thynnus, 1325, **1329**
Thysanophrys cirronasus, **1817**
Tiger puffer, **104**
Tigerfishes, 222, 1887
Tilefishes, 531
Tinker's butterflyfish, **378**
Toadfishes, 1821
TORPEDINIDAE, 1067
Torpedo tokionis, **1068**
Torpedos, 1067
Toxotes, 328
Toxotes chatareus, **327, 328**
Toxotes jaculator, **327**
TOXOTIDAE, 327
Trachichthodes affinis, 1161
Trachinocephalus, 335, 959
Trachinocephalus myops, **336, 916**
Trachinotus bailloni, **430, 813**
Trachinotus blochii, **1459**
Trachurus japonicus, **432**
TRIACANTHIDAE, 391
Triacanthus aculeatus, 391
Triacanthus anomalus, **392**
Triacanthus biaculeatus, **391**
Triacanthus brevirostris, **392**
Triaenodon obesus, **1671**
TRIAKIDAE, 504
Triakis scyllia, **507**
Triangle butterflyfish, **57, 378**
TRICHIURIDAE, 927
Trichiurus lepturus, **928**
Tridentiger trigonocephalus, **174**
Triggerfishes, 114, 815, **1630**
TRIGLIDAE, 511
Triodon bursarius, **1357**
Triple-tailed wrasse, **572**
Tripletails, 1265
Tripterodon, 1139
Tripterygion bapturum, **169**
Tripterygion etheostoma, 162, **473**
Trisotropis dermopterus, **1251**
Tri-spot wrasse, **440**
Tropidinus zonatus, **436**
Trumpetfishes, 773, 1799, 1780
Trunkfishes, 97, 1899
Trygonorrhina, 1677
Trygonorrhina fasciata, **1396**
TRYPTERYGIIDAE, 636
Tunas, 1325
Turbot, 263
Turkeyfish, 258, **265**, 512, 653
Twinspot cardinalfish, **242**
Twinspot damselfish, **204**
Twinspot wrasse, **141, 575**
Two-banded anemonefish, **704**
Two-lined snapper, 222, **223, 421**
Tylosurus giganteus, **332**
Tylosurus melanotus, **924**

Typee hawkfish, **488**

U
Undulate triggerfish, **119, 124**
Unicorn leather-jacket, **125**
Unicorn razorfish, **132**
Unicornfish, 89, **388**
Upeneichthys porosus, **1890**
Upeneus, 259, 739
Upeneus bensasi, **272, 970**
Upeneus moluccensis, **971, 972**
Upeneus tragula, **971, 1463, 1494**
Upeneus vittatus, **344**
URANOSCOPIDAE, 538
Uranoscopus bicinctus, **983**
Uranoscopus japonicus, **541, 981**
Urogymnus, 1673
Urogymnus africanus, 1673, **1675**
Urolophus, 1673
Urolophus aurantiacus, **509**
Urolophus testaceus, **1673**

V
Vagabond butterflyfish, **56, 376**
Vanderhorstia ornatissimus, **475**
Variegated lizardfish, **338**
Variegated wrasse, **441**
Variola, 643
Variola louti, **490, 1231, 1492**
Velvetfishes, 641
Verasper variegatus, **1096**
Vermiculated angelfish, **36, 37**
Vermiculated puffer, **409**
Vermiculated spinefoot, **389**
Violet-tinted soldierfish, **341**
Vireosa hanae, **475**

W
Wetmorella ocellata, **1580**
Wart-skin frogfish, **530**
Weevers, 467, 777
White-blotch moray eel, **354**
White-cheeked moray, **350**
White-faced surgeonfish, **91**
White-rim triggerfish, **120**
White-spotted boxfish, **101**
White-spotted tang, **88**
White-tailed damselfish, **202**
Whitings, **1003**
Wispy scorpionfish, **517**
Wistari Reef, **1659**
Wobbegongs, 501, 1399, 1666
Wrasses, 128, 569, **1570**, 1729
Wrought-iron butterflyfish, **53**

X
Xanthichthys mento, **118**
Xanthichthys ringens, 1345, **1627**
Xanthichthys sp., **1627**
Xiphasia matsubarai, **466**
    (See *Xiphasia setifer*)
Xiphasia setifer, **466**
Xiphias gladius, **1258**
XIPHIIDAE, 1260
Xyrichthys taeniourus, **149, 867,**
    868, 869

(See *Hemipteronotus
    taeniourus*)

Y
Yellow-backed damselfish, **203**
Yellow-belly, **439**
Yellow conger eel, **352**
Yellow devil, **196**
Yellow-finned jack, **429**
Yellowfin goby, **179**
Yellow head angelfish, **35**
Yellow-lined sweetlips, **348**
Yellow-lined tripodfish, **392**
Yellow-mouthed moray, **353**
Yellow porgy, **438**
Yellow puffer, **403**
Yellow-streaked monocle-bream,
    421
Yellow-striped caesio, **223**
Yellow-striped snapper, **226**
Yellowtail, **427, 428**
Yellow-tailed anemonefish, **180, 185**
Yellow-tailed blenny, **469**
Yellow-tailed blue devil, **203**
Yellow-tailed cleaner, **447**
Yerutius, 219
Yongeichthys criniger, **1602**
Ypsiscarus ovifrons, **985**

Z
ZANCLIDAE, 75, 810
Zanclus, 75
Zanclus canescens, 75, **77, 810, 811,**
    812, 1156, 1157, 1605, 1750, 1751
Zebra goby, **179, 472**
Zebra lionfish, 265
Zebra moray, **354**
Zebra morwong, **247**
Zebra-striped Port Jackson shark,
    506
Zebrasoma, 797
Zebrasoma desjardinii, **84, 799**
Zebrasoma flavescens, **84, 385,**
    1150, 1151
Zebrasoma scopas, **84, 88, 800,**
    1150, 1151, 1152, 1606, 1749
Zebrasoma veliferum, **89, 91, 1748**
Zebrasoma veliferum, **84**
    (See *Zebrasoma desjardinii*)
Zebrasoma xanthurum, **384, 798**
Zebrias zebra, **1100**
Zeus japonicus, **550**
Zigzag wrasse, **454, 609**
Zoarchias veneficus, **161**
Zonogobius boreus, **178**